C000021516

# THE SELF-BUILDER

# THE SELF-BUILDER

## How to Build Your Own Home and Halve the Cost

Nicholas Snelgar

**DAVID & CHARLES**
Newton Abbot  London

# ACKNOWLEDGEMENTS

I wish to express my extreme gratitude for the help and advice I have received from the following: R. Ashton, MA, Dip Arch (Cantab), RIBA; W. R. Ellis, MCIOB, MBIM; C. G. Hill, NIC, EIC; Vanessa Fison; G. R. Knapman, FRICS; Nancy Lawton; G. G. Porcher; J. Powell; A. Safe, RP; E. D. Short; Charles Campbell who produced the drawings; and to my parents for their unfailing support.

My thanks are due to the following organisations for granting me permission to use material from their publications: Sam Smith (Builder's Detail Sheets Series 1 and 2, International Thompson Publishing); British Standards Institution, Linford Ward, Milton Keynes MK14 6LE; Wednesdbury Tube Company, Park Royal Road, London NW10 7JY; Hepworth Plastics Limited; Cowley Limited; Entec Limited.

**For Lory and Tess**

Whilst every attempt has been made to ensure that all information
and prices are correct at the time of going to press, the
author and publishers can accept no responsibility for any
errors or omissions.

**British Library Cataloguing in Publication Data**

Snelgar, Nicholas
  The self builder.
  1. House construction – Amateurs'
  manuals  2. Architecture, Domestic –
  Designs and plans
  I. Title
  728.3    TH4815

  ISBN 0-7153-8765-0

  ISBN 0–7153–9794 X

© Nicholas Snelgar, 1987

First published 1987
Second impression 1989

All rights reserved. No part of this
publication may be reproduced, stored
in a retrieval system, or transmitted,
in any form or by any means, electronic,
mechanical, photocopying, recording or
otherwise, without the prior permission
of David & Charles Publishers plc

Typeset by Typesetters (Birmingham) Ltd, Smethwick, West Midlands
and printed in Great Britain
by Redwood Burn Ltd, Trowbridge
for David & Charles Publishers plc
Brunel House  Newton Abbot  Devon

# CONTENTS

| | | |
|---|---|---:|
| | More Ways Than One | 6 |
| 1 | Site and Scene | 7 |
| 2 | Design and Building Programme | 14 |
| 3 | Let's Build | 30 |
| 4 | Construction of Walls | 56 |
| 5 | The Roof | 87 |
| 6 | First Fix | 106 |
| 7 | Plastering | 128 |
| 8 | Second Fix | 134 |
| 9 | Outside Work | 150 |
| 10 | Other Experiences | 152 |
| | Further Reading | 157 |
| | Index | 159 |

# MORE WAYS THAN ONE

We think of our housing as being off the peg, and served up to us in impressive brochures or displayed in shiny High Street windows. We have grown up with the tradition of the developer solving our housing needs. There is another way. A growing band of individuals are discovering the self-build approach to the housing question. This book is aimed at them.

The structure referred to as Hancocks is the house I built and, where possible, I have used uncomplicated materials to illustrate the method of building rather than to provide an extensive list of all available products to serve a certain purpose. I have recommended materials that can be assembled without specialist knowledge and I have excluded various alternatives, not because they are inferior, but because they require prior experience to obtain a high-quality finish.

This book is not intended to be a textbook of building methods, but rather a probe into modern construction, answering problems that I encountered and stimulating further research into particular areas of interest.

I hope this book inspires many more people to join the self-build movement across the country. Many families already derive enormous satisfaction from building their own houses, extensions and garages, testing their abilities far beyond the confinement of twentieth-century consumer living.

# 1
# SITE AND SCENE

If you ask a self-builder why he has worked hard for seventy hours a week over the past year in appalling conditions, why he has herded his family into a caravan, you will be met by a torrent of answers divided into fifty per cent financial benefits and fifty per cent adventure, independence and desire to tackle a huge project.

The opportunity to earn 'capital' is enormous. In two years it is possible to house your family in spacious surroundings as well as earning collateral against which to borrow money for funding a business venture. Recent legislation has enabled the building societies to lend money, on property, for financing businesses. By building your own house you are sure to get value for money. Your money goes further. You can follow your ideas on design while keeping within the planning requirements; you can install top-quality insulation in the roof space, perhaps 200mm (8in) instead of the bare minimum to meet the regulation requirements; you can build in double glazed windows; you can provide closed-in porches at each external door and you can provide many items, considered to be luxury in the developer market, for very small extra outlay. On a purely philosophical front, the house you live in must as near as possible meet your daily requirements. You can limit the sources of irritation as far as possible. I think the self-builder, once he decides to follow that path, becomes more curious about the structure in which he lives: he wants to know how it works; he wants to know what everything is. It becomes another mystery to solve, another hurdle of knowledge to leap.

The lone self-builder far outnumbers the self-build associations. The main problems for the individual, rather than the group, is to obtain building land. Since 1947 all new buildings and extensions and modifications to old ones have to comply with planning laws. These are designed to restrict random development, to preserve areas of outstanding natural beauty and to organise buildings for certain uses into sensible groups. The planning Acts are administered by each local authority throughout the country, the idea being to control growth in housing and industrial building so as to provide a harmony between residential areas and areas of high industrial activity, between the hearts of medieval towns and the move towards supermarket retailing, between car-parking and ring road development. All aspects of development should fit into the great plan. As a result you cannot buy an orchard from a farmer and necessarily expect to build a house. You must ensure that the land will have at least 'outline planning consent' before you purchase it. The land, not the applicant, bears the consent or lack of consent. It is possible to negotiate a position on a field whereby you apply and receive 'outline planning consent' before you purchase the field. 'Outline consent' means that in the eyes of the local authority planning committee the land in question may accommodate a building the exact nature of which will be decided later. At the time of outline consent, no doubt many conditions will be established which will have a binding effect on the structure that eventually rises from the soil. The conditions may be too onerous for the self-builder to meet. They may insist on a building quite unsuitable for his needs or quite outside his pocket.

Approach all farmers and all landowners in the area. This is the most trying time; you must let it be known that you are seeking a building plot. I know a man who after a year of searching found a dilapidated bungalow built in 1930 on a quarter of an acre. He was able to buy it, demolish the bungalow and build a house. Planning consent was obtained without difficulty and the plot was valued as a building site, ignoring the presence of a tumbledown dwelling. This is not always the case. If you can prove that a site has been used as a dwelling since 1948 then the local authority is almost bound to grant you permission to build or, if not, to pay compensation for a change of policy.

It is absolutely essential to employ a solicitor to check the title of the land you intend to buy. He or she must be satisfied that there are no restrictive covenants or easements attached to the plot which may prevent you from building in a certain way. The solicitor will carry out a host of 'searches' that will interrogate the local authority as to their future plans for the area and the plot in question. This should unearth previous attempts at obtaining planning permission or road building schemes or gravel-quarrying rights that may be owned by someone else who may wish to invoke them at any time.

Estate agents deal with a small number of plots and generally they have developers on their books who are competing with the self-builder for land. Local authorities may have individual plots for sale. It is more productive, however, to carry out a physical search for suitable land. You may spot a small field or wild patch of brambles and you could actually suggest to the owner that this might be a potential building plot. This is the hardest part. If you come through the business of finding a site then you are well on the road to success. To purchase the land you may have savings, or you may have to raise a second mortgage on your existing house. Somehow you have to raise that money on your own. No financial organisation that I have spoken to will lend money to buy the land. The self-builder has no track record in building, and they feel that your contribution to the project should shape itself in the form of ownership of the land.

No amount of advice, no amount of lecturing, will be much help in the quest for building land. Choose a very large area, preferably outside a 'green belt', which designates a zone on the planning map wherein no development shall take place. Move restlessly over your area of choice and talk to people. Read local newspapers, relentlessly pursue the land-owners and try to suggest potential sites, look for buildings in disrepair, knock on doors; search and eventually you will find a site.

The alternative method of approach, if all this searching is too much, is to join or form a 'self-build association'. The formation of one such association is related in Chapter 10. It must consist of seven or more individuals and so you must want to live on an estate of houses of not less than seven units. An association does, on the face of it, have more chance of obtaining land as local authorities are obliged to aid local self-build groups under a Department of Environment circular put out in 1975.

Having purchased the land with outline planning consent and having made absolutely sure you understand the conditions imposed on the builder, such as overall height of any dwelling, overall size, access for motor vehicles and any rights of way, you can begin to familiarise yourself with the area and formulate ideas about style and the size of house you intend to build. Which way should it face? Where are the services coming from? However, the fundamental question of supply of water and electricity should be sorted out before purchase, to ensure that no enormous expense will be incurred later. Seek legal advice at every phase of the search for land.

Next you must get some sketches on paper. Approach a draughtsman working in their spare time, or a local architect, preferably working alone. Qualified architects will have the letters RIBA after their name, denoting membership of the professional body known as the Royal Institute of British Architects. These professional people are familiar with dealing in planning applications and may well be known by officials of the local authority. A local architect will be up to date on the current requirements and thinking of the local planning office and can therefore direct their client along a path which will end in planning approval. First ask the professional of your choice to put together a sketch scheme based on your ideas and drawings. Spend plenty of time talking the points through, visiting the site and pursuing the style you have chosen. Decide on a final drawing and instruct the architect to apply for planning permission. While this process is under way you should be out on the streets finding finance for the building project. You must have detailed costings of the whole job. How are you going to approach the work? You have two choices: either you attempt the majority of the work yourself, and this book sets out to make this possible, or you act as a manager and engage subcontractors to execute each stage of the work in a steady, well-organised flow. Whatever finance you eventually find the company concerned will insist upon professional supervision of the building work to ensure that it is up to the standard of NHBC approved work. The National House-Building Council was set up as an independent body to monitor the work of its member builders who subscribe to the organisation, and to issue a certificate to verify the standard of work carried out. The NHBC has an army of inspectors who make periodic site visits and who compile a report on the building which is to be certified, and it is not economically feasible for a self-builder involved in only one unit to become a member. An architect or suitably qualified person must inspect the site and report to the finance institution to reassure them that the finished building will be of the highest standard. The NHBC produce a handbook which clearly sets out their standards. It is well worth buying, and is listed in the Further Reading section on p 157.

Once planning consent is granted the architect or draughtsman should be instructed to prepare the working drawings to submit to the building control department of the local authority. All new buildings must comply with the Building Regulations. The professional will be familiar with the regulations and will provide adequate detail on the drawings to satisfy the building control department. A building inspector will visit the site at your request to inspect various specified stages of the work. Building inspectors cannot be made liable for commercial loss and this should be borne in mind when seeking their advice. You will be given a set of postcards which will summon the inspector when each phase is complete and ready for inspection. It is your duty to give the inspector adequate warning of a stage reaching completion. On no account progress to the next stage before he has visited the site. Subcontractors are able to work out prices for their various tasks from these working drawings. Always get three separate subcontractors to quote for each job.

**Drawings**

To accompany a planning application:

    Location plan, scale 1 : 2,500 showing position of building in relation to surrounding features.

    Site plan, scale 1 : 500 showing boundaries, existing trees, drainage and outhouses.

Elevation drawings, scale 1 : 100 showing each face of building, north, south, east and west.

To obtain building control approval:

Ground floor plan, scale 1 : 50 showing every detail of construction together with explanatory notes.

First floor plan, scale 1 : 50 showing every detail as above. Elevations as above and sections showing construction details.

In some cases additional information may be required by the building inspector. Once building control approval is obtained ask your architect/draughtsman to run off plenty of copies of the drawings.

## Finance

I have to assume you have already bought the land, because there really is very little help for the self-builder who has not purchased his land through his own endeavours. Once you have the land, with building permission, you will almost certainly find a finance company to support the building project. When you approach a financial institution you must enter the meeting as a businessman. They are used to dealing with businessmen, so do not imagine that the managers are particularly interested in your unusual approach to the world of housing. They will lend you money largely on their appraisal of your personality. They will judge you on ability to manage money and on commitment. They are only interested in your ability to complete the project when the risk is over and the house is worth twice the cost. They can breathe a sigh of relief and hook you up to a twenty-five-year mortgage, and the shareholders will be happy. People tend to take the line of least resistance in life, especially managers of finance who have a career structure to follow. It is easier to lend money to safe bets. Self-builders are unknown performers. They may be excellent teachers or first-class mechanics, but can they manage huge sums of money and will their enthusiasm carry them through the nine to twelve months ahead? The managers are assessing you, not your prime building site overlooking the Quantock Hills. As you only have half an hour to show your wares you must go in there totally prepared. Carry a file or briefcase. Don't rummage: have the drawings and costings and planning approvals to hand. Your costings must be absolutely clear. By now you should have built the house in words and lists.

In Chapter 2 we discuss the materials in order of need and the calculations for arriving at quantities. Use these calculations to determine the quantities for costing purposes. Builders' merchants will be happy to work out the price of all materials. Send details to three companies, not just one. If you prepare a master list based on Chapter 2 you can work out costs and use the list for ordering materials when you commence work. Be prepared with lists of tasks you will perform and tasks you will invite subcontractors to do. Have your motives for building your own house clearly in your mind. Avoid being woolly and philosophical. The finance company will want to know that their money is safe. The last thing they need is a half-finished building which is an asset to no one.

## Building Societies

Most building societies will now lend money in instalments to finance the actual building work. Formerly it was normal to obtain building finance from a bank on the understanding that a building society would take over the long-term finance and pay off the bank loan. Two building societies out of the many approached felt that self-build was not such a high risk, as the standard of work is so high and the end product is usually more valuable than similar buildings in the developer sector. Here are typical requirements:

1. Architect supervision.
2. Money issued on architect's certificate in four instalments:
   (a) First floor joists
   (b) Roofed in
   (c) Plastering complete
   (d) All works complete.
3. Interest on building monies charged at half a per cent over minimum lending rate (MLR).
4. Interest payment usually taken out of last instalment.
5. The extent of the final mortgage will depend on the society's criteria regarding total earning power of the individual.

## High Street Banks

The banks are trying to move into the long-term mortgage market and to this extent they are mildly interested in self-build projects. They, to a man, consider the self-builder venture to be in a very high risk category. They will charge four per cent above MLR, in contrast to the attitude of the building societies, and will closely scrutinise the earning capabilities of the individual. Here is a list of requirements gleaned first hand from one of the 'big four':

1. Sound estimates including margins.
2. Valuation of end result.
3. Architect's supervision throughout.
4. Interested in long-term mortgage business.
5. Will handle all insurance business.

6. Establish income criteria at outset.
7. May ask for independent estimate of building costs.
8. Release money in three stages:
   (a) Roofed in
   (b) Plastered
   (c) Finished.
9. Under certain circumstances they may lend half the cost of the land.
10. Formula for payments is as follows:
    (a) At the roofed in stage they release two-thirds of the cost of the building up to the roof.
    (b) When the building is plastered they will release two-thirds of the cost to this point.
    (c) When the building has been decorated they will release two-thirds of the cost of finishing. On completion they release the remainder minus interest.

So, following this route you must finance half the land plus the cost of getting the roof on from your own resources.

It is unwise to go it alone at this stage. The financiers are not impressed by lone self-builders riding into the eye of the storm. Make quite sure that your architect is fully aware of the extent of your budget. Try not to hurry the design and sketch scheme stage. It is far cheaper to sort out differences when the drawings are in embryo. Prepare accurate, well-detailed drawings from which you can produce an accurate bill of quantities listing all the materials. From an accurate bill of quantities arise sound, professional costings and estimates arriving at the final figure which you need to borrow.

**Insurance**
You must insure the building at all stages against damage from tempest, flood and fire. You must insure against causing any injury to subcontractors or members of the public who may stray or be invited on to your site.

This is called public liability insurance and many leading insurance companies will provide this cover. It is essential that you take out a life assurance policy to cover the cost of building the house in the event of your dying with the building incomplete, leaving your dependants with a huge financial problem. Seek advice on this very important matter.

# 2
# DESIGN AND BUILDING PROGRAMME

**Design**

The decisions you make at the design stage will shape your building into a useful, habitable dwelling. Let us enter into a general discussion about the factors governing your design.

The main unrelenting factor and limitation on translating your wildest dreams into a modern building is money. Here, we have got to steer a course through all the available methods of constructing each stage and arrive at the simplest, most pleasing, structure that falls both inside our capabilities as self-builders and within our budget.

Before you visit your architect or draughtsman you should prepare a list of ideas. All our lives we are harvesting likes and dislikes from the experiences we have of other people's houses. List any features you wish to include in your design. You should decide on every aspect of the building, from its position on the site down to the door handles. No last-minute, forced issues. When you start building there will be no time to browse through ironmongery catalogues, or to stroll through kitchen and bathroom showrooms.

The siting of the building must allow for the rising and setting of the sun. In the six months of winter you want to harvest as much light as possible into the living rooms. Is it possible to orientate the building to face south-east? Have the rooms in which you live bathed in sunlight. Try not to sacrifice too much of the site to the motor car. Do you want your garden in front of or behind the house? Such fundamental decisions must not be sources of regret later.

Dig trial holes on the plot to try and define the nature of the subsoil. This is an area where costs can rise sharply should deeper footings prove necessary.

For simplicity and therefore cheapness, rectangular buildings with straight gables and a pitched roof are leaders in the category. You may wish to design with a view to building on extensions at a later date to increase the amount of accommodation. Next you must decide between conventional cavity wall construction using facing bricks and internal blocks, and timber frame construction. In Scandinavia and the northern

14

states of North America they experience cold dry winters and hot dry summers. The relative humidity is low throughout the year. In Britain we suffer enormous rainfall and high humidity. Timber frame houses perform well in Scandinavian type climates where the timber is seldom subject to dampness in the atmosphere and where standards of timber and timber 'drying' are high. In Britain the timber is kiln-dried, but is then subjected to high humidity in the atmosphere, which causes movement. Timber frames offer high insulation values and are quick and easy to erect, but they fall down on performance in this damp, rainy climate. From the cost point of view there is little difference. If you opt for the brick and block construction you have to achieve a certain thermal efficiency, which is laid down in the Building Regulations 1985 as being $0.6W/m^2{}^\circ C$ (the Kelvin scale is used in some documents; $K = {}^\circ C + 273$). Every building material has a measure of thermal efficiency, which is defined as its U-value. The U-value is the thermal transmittance of a material measured in watts per square metre, degrees Celsius. The U-value of a material or combination of materials is found by adding up the resistances that each material offers. The resistance is the thickness of the materials divided by the conductivity. So, in order to achieve a U-value on our external walls of $0.6W/m^2{}^\circ C$, we either have to fill the cavity with insulation material as we build or use a lightweight insulation block, on the inner skin of the cavity wall, that is 150mm (6in) thick. The purpose of the cavity is to act as a barrier against dampness. It may therefore be a disadvantage to stuff the cavity full of insulating material, and the attitude of many professional builders is to opt for the 150mm internal block to provide the correct U-value.

The inner and outer skins of the cavity wall are held together by wall ties. Cases of premature wall tie failure are cropping up where galvanised steel ties have rusted and expansion of the rusting objects has pushed the walls apart. The cost of putting this right is enormous, and therefore it may be wise to use polypropylene wall ties. Further discussion with your architect is advisable.

The size of the rooms may to some extent be governed by the position of load-bearing walls which will support the roof and this is where your professional adviser will be an enormous help in summarising what is and what is not possible. You will want to build as big a house as will suit the site and as many square feet of living space as your budget will allow. With any luck you can reckon on self-building costs of between £14 and £16 per square foot (11sq ft = 1sq m), depending on how much of the work you attempt and how much you let out to subcontractors.

The ground floor of a building will either be what is termed 'solid', which means it is constructed of concrete upon a horizontal damp-proof membrane, or it will be a 'suspended timber floor', which means it is raised up above the concrete 'oversite' on wooden joists and finished with timber boards. A concrete floor is cold and unyielding to the human foot, but is cheap and simple to construct. It is possible to increase the thermal efficiency by incorporating a layer of 25mm (1in) polystyrene board between the oversite and the screed. Suspended floors on the other hand are constructed of wood with inherent thermal properties; they cushion the human step and they have a free air space underneath them to carry all pipework that would otherwise be firmly buried in a solid floor. It is important that water authority regulations should be consulted as some byelaws may prevent the burying of water pipes). They are more expensive to construct but careful cost comparisons should be made before making a decision. Suspended floors are immeasurably more comfortable.

Joinery items such as external door frames and windows will be 'off the peg', purchased from a specialist company. Gather as many brochures as you can and compare the styles and the prices. Double-glazed units can be fitted at the factory. The timber around the window glass will have to have a deeper rebate to accept the extra thickness of the double-glazed unit and so either the timbers will be weaker or the window construction more expensive, employing stouter timber. When you have fitted these factory-glazed units you will have the problem of draughts through the point where the window opens, which will get worse as the timbers move and twist during the natural process of drying out. Secondary double glazing which is applied to the inside of the window makes more sense for the self-build dwelling. Draughts will be excluded, and sound insulation greatly improved. While discussing windows it is important to agree on the height of the internal window board or sills. Usually the term 'sill' applies to the outside detail whereas 'window board' refers to the inside. The window heads should all line up on any one elevation (face of the building) where possible. Different rooms require different sill heights: in a kitchen you need window sills that coincide with standard worktop heights from floor level, while in the ground floor living rooms they should be lower, to enable you to see out when in a sitting position. Each window might have a shallow arch of brickwork above it as a feature, although anything that deviates from straightforward brickwork is difficult and costly. Keep it simple.

Internal joinery items such as skirting boards and architraves may be decorative, with exquisite mouldings machined into them, or they can be plain as Fig 47a shows. The heavily moulded architrave must be cut at exactly 45° otherwise none of the lines and rolls will match up. If you are going to fix it yourself, are you able to make a good job?

For a little more expense you can build a traditional roof, instead of using modern truss rafters which are much easier and quicker to raise.

Truss rafters could be said to be stronger as all the joints are made on a factory bench, whereas the traditional roof relies on good workmanship to give it strength. The roof space above a dwelling employing truss rafters is totally wasted: it is full of timbers none of which may be removed to facilitate access. Is it not short-sighted to lose that storage space in order to save two extra days' labour? What kind of insulation are you going to provide in the roof space? The minimum requirement in new houses is 100mm (4in) but twice that thickness would be a more satisfactory target.

The provision of chimneys gives both ventilation and a secondary heat source to the central heating. If you locate them within the building you will lose space and gain all the heat, but they are more difficult to build. If you build them externally on each gable you gain the space but lose some of the heat, and have an easier time constructing the chimney. I recommend a chimney at either end of the rectangular building, one serving the central heating appliance and the other serving an open fire.

Stud partitions made of timber framing should be avoided where possible, because the sound insulation from one room to another is poor. If you have to use stud partitions, you might consider fixing a layer of 18mm (¾in) chipboard to the studs before fixing the plasterboard. This improves the sound insulation.

You must design for the installation of a central heating system even if you only build in the basic pipework at first (or ducting in the case of warm air), and add the radiators and heat source later.

All these aspects of the building must be discussed with your architect. Do not leave it to him or her when choosing the facing bricks to be used throughout the building but try and see some examples of the brick in use. All this care and thought will show up in the final product as a shining example of good design.

**The people involved and the tasks they perform**
A self-build project must have targets. Potential sources of finance will expect to see target dates and some sort of building programme. A lone builder attempting to build a two-storey house enclosing a thousand square feet of living space should aim to 'break the ground' in the spring. Then maximising his effort through the long summer days, and assuming the bricklaying is subcontracted out, he should have the building 'dry' by November and it should be possible to complete the work by the following June. This is a very general target as so much depends upon the weather. I am assuming that the construction work will be carried out in the self-builder's spare time. Remember, self-build associations manage to clock up thirty-one hours per week throughout the project. This is relentless – week in, week out. If you take much

longer than fifteen months, the interest on the borrowed money begins to eat into the budget. You have to strike a sensible balance between the tasks you can attempt and the jobs best carried out by experienced sub-contractors.

Here is a list of tradesmen in the order they will be needed on site, with a brief description of the tasks they are qualified to attempt. Should you wish to engage any one of them you must make it clear whether they are to provide labour and materials or labour only.

### *Excavator* or JCB digger

He is an owner-driver who is usually hired by the hour. You may need a tipper lorry to haul away excavated material. The digger-driver will recommend a hired lorry. Some hand digging will be necessary to tidy and straighten and firm up the trenches.

### *Concretor*

He will undertake to concrete the foundations and to concrete the oversite slab.

### *Drainlayer*

He lays all surface water and foul drains and any ducts needed for services (gas, electricity, water and telephone).

Excavator, concretor and drainlayer may be joined together in one firm called 'groundworkers'. They would tackle all aspects of the building up to damp-proof course level.

### *Bricklayer*

He follows the groundworker in that his work begins as soon as the concrete is hard in the footings. In fact, quite often a gang of bricklayers will concrete the footings, then bring the cavity blockwork up to the damp-proof course, which is 150mm (6in) above ground level. The bricklayer is responsible for building the cavity walls right up to wall-plate height, including gables and chimneys. He will build in all external door frames, windows and joists as he goes, and is responsible for fixing all damp-proof courses wherever they may be necessary.

### *Scaffolder*

Again bricklayers will often build in their own scaffolding as they go. Conversely you can hire the tubing from a scaffolding company, together with the men to erect it. The scaffolders would be expected to return each time a new 'lift' or platform is needed.

*Carpenter*
Good carpenters are always fiendishly busy. Choose carefully and get your firm order in quickly. At all times leave your contractors in no doubt as to the programme and the targets. Half the battle is to achieve a steady uninterrupted flow of labour and materials. The carpenter will first be summoned to cut and fix the chamber joists. Thereafter, he can disappear until the bricklayers have bedded on the wall-plate. He will build the roof, fix the stairs, nail down the floors, hang doors, fix architraves and skirting boards, fix down window boards and fit kitchen units.

*Tiler*
He fixes roofing felt and battens, then follows on by fixing the tiles. He may be in a position to obtain enormous discounts from his suppliers and it may be an advantage to allow him to supply the tiles.

*Electrician*
As soon as the roof is watertight the electrician may begin to chase out the walls for all cable runs. He will return after the plasterer to complete the wiring.

*Plumber*
He must get the building 'carcassed out' for both the domestic supply of hot and cold water and for central heating ahead of the plasterer. He is responsible for all lead flashings and for fixing rainwater gutters and downpipes. It is his job to connect all the sanitary ware to the drains which the groundworkers will have positioned, correctly, in the oversite concrete.

*Plasterer*
He fixes all plasterboard and applies rendering coats followed by a top coat of fine wall plaster to all walls. Ceilings receive a top coat only. He will also, as a final job, lay a sand and cement screed on top of the oversite to finish off the ground floor. This will not apply if you are having suspended floors.

*Glazier*
To supply glass and to fix it in a house is so cheap that on no account is it worth attempting yourself. If you are going to stain the windows instead of painting them be careful to order the correct putty.

*Floorlayer*
He lays vinyl tiles, vinyl sheeting, quarry tiles and woodblock flooring to

the floor surfaces provided. Some floorlayers will prefer to lay their own screed before fixing the floor tiles to ensure that the surface is absolutely level. The floorlayer is the last contractor before the decorator.

### Decorator
He applies the final finishes: varnish, oil-based paint and emulsion paint on the walls and ceiling. There must be as little dust as possible when the decorator is on site. All other trades should have completed.

Most commercial building contracts are summarised in a document called a 'specification', which is drawn up by an architect and contains a precise description of how each task should be executed, what standard is expected and what materials must be used. This is only really necessary if you are intending to get involved in the 'tendering' process where several building companies are asked to quote for the entire job. It does not apply to the self-builder; however, a clear idea of acceptable standards should be laid down.

## The Materials Required
Next we must consider the materials we shall need throughout the building process. At every step you must anticipate the materials required, which have to be ordered in advance. Anything can suddenly become scarce in the building industry. Joinery items must be ordered at least six weeks before they will be needed and transport must be sorted out. Bricks may take ages to emerge from their kiln. Try to order the total number of bricks on one order. The various materials required are discussed below in chronological order, together with some calculations to determine quantities.

### Concrete for foundations
Take the total length of all foundation trenches (scale off the ground floor plan using a metric scale rule for costings). Allow for a depth of 300mm (12in) of concrete. Measure the average width of the trench.

As an example, consider a 1,000sq ft two-storey house with two load-bearing cross walls, which must have their own foundations.

Total length of foundation trenches= 31.4m (103ft)
Average width of trenches        = 600mm (2ft)
Depth of concrete              = 300mm (12in)
Therefore, $31.4 \times 0.600 \times 0.300$  = 5.65m$^3$.

The ratio of aggregate to cement for foundations should be 1 : 8, ie one part cement to eight parts aggregate. When ordering truck-mixed concrete allow a ten per cent margin for the fact that your trenches are not absolutely square and straight. In the case of the above example order 6m$^3$, which is a full truck-load. You are usually penalised by as much as £7 per cubic metre not carried in the truck so it pays to have a full load if possible. It is an excellent piece of planning to have a secondary area ready to receive concrete to accommodate any surplus, in the event that your calculations are slightly over the mark.

The above method of ordering truck-mixed concrete can be strongly recommended. However, here is an example using the same figures to enable you to calculate how much aggregate and how much cement to order should you wish to mix the concrete yourself. The volume of material needed to pour the foundation = 5.65m$^3$. A ratio of 1 : 8 cement to aggregate is needed. If we divide 5.65m$^3$ by nine (ie nine parts) we get one part being 0.62m$^3$ and eight parts being 4.96m$^3$. The cement portion of this mix is therefore 0.62m$^3$. A bag of cement weighing 50kg represents a volume of 0.035m$^3$ powder; 0.62/0.035 = 17.7, say eighteen bags. Order 5m$^3$ aggregate from the gravel pit. Note that in certain ground conditions you may have to use sulphate-resisting cement.

*Class 'A' Concrete Blocks up to Damp-proof Course*
For the external skin of a cavity wall a 100mm (4in) dense concrete block measuring 450mm × 225mm × 100mm (18in × 9in × 4in) is used. They are still referred to in the building industry as 18 × 9 × 4 blocks. For the internal skin of a cavity wall use blocks as above if your internal light-weight block is 100mm (4in) thick. If on the other hand you decide to use 150mm (6in) lightweight blocks to achieve your 0.6Wm$^2$°C U-value then you must order 140mm (5½in) dense concrete blocks for use below the damp-proof course; 150mm blocks are unavailable.

To calculate the number of blocks required, first measure perimeter and cross walls to arrive at a total length. Divide that figure by the length of a block. This gives you the number of blocks in a course. Multiply by the number of courses required to reach the damp-proof course. Refer-ring back to our example, we have a total wall length of 31.4m; 31.4/0.45 (ie 450mm) = 69.7, say seventy blocks to the course (the word 'course' refers to one layer of blocks, bricks or tiles). Let us suppose we had to dig a trench a metre deep. Take off 300mm for the concrete footings. That leaves 700mm to be divided by 225mm (9in), which is the height of each course of blocks.

700/225 = 3.1, say three courses.
Therefore 3 × 70  = 210 blocks for the outer skin
        plus        210 blocks for the inner skin
gives                420 blocks to order (ten blocks to square metre).

Remember to distinguish between 100mm and 140mm blocks.

*Damp-proof Course (DPC)*
This is 100mm (4in) wide. The best quality is pitch polymer DPC, which is sold in 20m rolls. On our example house you would need 31.4 × 2/20 = 3.14, say four rolls. If you intend to build suspended timber floors then each sleeper wall will need a damp-proof course.

*Building Sand*
It is wise to order the total amount of building sand needed to build the whole house, as loads of sand from different parts of the pit may vary in colour. Each square metre of brickwork requires 0.02m³ cement mortar to lay it. For every concrete block you lay it is equivalent to laying six bricks. A square metre of blockwork will require 0.02/6 = 0.003m³ mortar.

Below the DPC we shall require, on our example house, 42 × 0.003 = 0.13m³ mortar; above the DPC 171m² facing bricks (see calculations for bricks) × 0.02 = 3.4m³ mortar are needed. At a ratio of 6 : 1 sand to cement we need 2.84m³ sand, say 3m³ or 4.7 tonnes. This must be multiplied by two to allow for the inner skin.

*Wall Ties*
Butterfly wall ties come in bundles of 250. Building regulations state that they must be positioned not more than 900mm (36in) apart horizontally and 450mm (18in) vertically, except at openings in the cavity wall where they must be not more than 300mm (12in) vertically. If we allow for six ties per square metre of cavity wall our example house will require 31.4 × 4.9 × 6 = 923, or four bundles. There is a possibility of wall tie failure as the building ages and to avoid this you could use stainless steel ties, which are expensive, or polypropylene ties, which are cheap. As the galvanised wall ties rust they expand and may push out the face brickwork. It is worth considering.

*External Door Frames*
These can be purchased from the same joinery company used when ordering windows. They must be on site by the time the oversite is laid. Each frame has a hard sill complete with waterbar. Make sure they are braced at the corners to keep them square.

*To 'Fill' the site prior to laying the oversite concrete*
Use 40mm (1½in) rejects from your local quarry or gravel pit. Rejects are clean, loose stones. Measure the area enclosed by the cavity wall, and multiply by the depth of stone needed to bring the level up to 100mm (4in) below the damp-proof course.

*Oversite Concrete*

This is the area enclosed by the cavity walls multiplied by 100mm, which is the thickness of the concrete slab to be laid, and is another candidate for truck-mixed concrete. For this purpose we need a ratio of 6 : 1 sand to cement.

*Polythene membrane to go beneath oversite concrete*

This is usually black polythene sheet but some local authorities will accept clear polythene. The best is PIFA grade black PVC sheeting in rolls of 100m² and with a thickness of 250μm (micrometres).

*Facing Bricks*

Calculate the area of facing bricks by multiplying the total length of the walls by the total height to the eaves. Add on the area of the gables. Multiply the total area by the number of bricks to the square metre, ie sixty. Add the area of the garage if applicable. It is wise to order all the facing bricks together to avoid any colour variation. They can take up to six months.

$$\begin{array}{rr} \text{House example: } 31.4 \times 5 \times 60 = & 9{,}420 \\ \text{Add gables} & 864 \\ \hline \text{Total facing bricks} & 10{,}284 \end{array}$$

By ignoring the openings in the cavity wall, we have made an allowance for wastage.

*Internal Blockwork*

These are normally 450mm × 225mm × 100mm (18in × 9in × 4in) with a thickness of 100mm (4in) or 150mm (6in). Brand names that spring to mind are Celcon and Thermalite. To calculate the quantity required take the surface area of the cavity wall in square metres. There are ten blocks to the square metre; allow ten per cent for wastage. The blocks will come direct from the works and will be off-loaded by crane.

*Flue Liners*

You must order these in plenty of time. They are made of clay and have a socket on one end and a rebate on the other. The dimensions are: height inclusive of rebate 300mm (12in), internal width 190mm (7½in) and external width 230mm (9in). Divide the height of the chimney by 300mm and multiply by the number of chimneys.

*Windows*

Prepare a window schedule as soon as you have agreed the style and size of windows. This schedule should list each room and its window allocation. You might also include details of the lintel over each window opening.

| | Height (mm) | Width (mm) | Lintel | Catalogue number |
|---|---|---|---|---|
| **Ground floor** | | | | |
| Sitting room | 1,200 | 1,769 | 2,219mm CN7 Catnic | 507AA |
| Dining room | 1,200 | 1,200 | 1,650mm Catnic CN7 | 510AC |
| Kitchen | 1,200 | 1,200 | | 510AC |
| Utility room | | | | |
| | etc | etc | etc | etc |
| WC | | | | |
| **First floor** | | | | |
| Bedroom 1 | | | | |
| Bedroom 2 | | | | |
| Bedroom 3 | | | | |
| Bathroom | | | | |
| Landing | | | | |

*Damp-proof course at Window and Door openings*
Pitch-polymer DPC in 20m rolls, 225mm (9in) wide. Measure the vertical height of all windows and doors.

*Frame Ties*
These come in sacks; numbers vary from merchant to merchant. Always order the screws at the same time as the ties. They are sometimes called 'frame cramps'. Use galvanised or sherardised screws.

*Scaffolding*
Taking as an example a two-storey house of 1,000sq ft with two gables, you will need 1,300ft (394m) of tubing with 66 scaffold boards each 3.9m long. This will provide you with a putlog scaffold.

Should you decide on an independent scaffold you will need 1,720ft (521m) of tubing plus 66 scaffold boards each 3.9m (12ft 9½in) long.

*Lintels*
Window and door openings in the cavity wall will require a combined metal lintel with a cavity tray designed to catch any moisture in the cavity and throw it to the outside skin, where it can escape through weep holes left in the mortar joints on the front edge of the lintel. Two of the most widely used lintels in this category are Dorman Long and Catnic. Both companies have very comprehensive catalogues and you will find it easy to match lintels to your openings. Make sure that you observe the correct 'bearing' for the lintel: this is the amount of overlap there is

between lintel and wall on either side of the opening. The minimum 'bearing' in all cases is 150mm (6in). Thus, when ordering lintels from a catalogue you take the width of the window or door frame and add 2 × 150mm to that length and find the nearest length of lintel to match your requirements. It may have to be longer; it must never be shorter.

For internal door openings the same rule regarding the minimum 'bearing' applies. You have a choice of corrugated metal lintels, which neatly span an opening, or pre-stressed concrete lintels, which are more common and come in a variety of lengths. Their cross-sectional dimensions are 100mm × 75mm (4in × 3in) and through the length of the lintel runs a pair of steel reinforcing rods. These lintels are available from 600mm (2ft) in length increasing to 3,300mm (10ft 9in) in steps of 150mm (6in). Most merchants will stock 600mm, 900mm, 1200mm, 1500mm and so on up to the maximum. You must always build at least three courses of brickwork above the concrete lintel to provide additional strength. Never use a concrete lintel where that is not possible.

One other type on the market is a metal box lintel, one course high (225mm) and suitable for bridging openings at eaves level, where only the inner leaf continues up to wall-plate height. They may also be used elsewhere for supporting blockwork on internal walls.

*First Floor Joists*

All structural timber in a modern building must be 'stress graded'. In a two-storey house, unless an architect or engineer intervenes, the timber must be graded to 'general structural' (GS) standard. This is covered by British Standard No BS4978, 'Timber grades for structural use'.

All sawn timber (timber that has not been planed) is sold in standard lengths of 3m, 3.7m, 4.3m, 4.9m and 5.1m. When ordering timber you must order to the nearest standard length, at all times keeping wastage to a minimum. The lengths of timber for first floor joists must be measured

**Fig 1** Timber Stress Grading Table

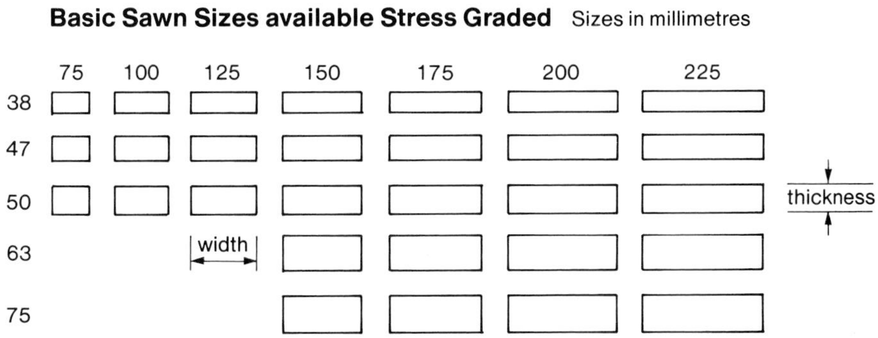

**Basic Sawn Sizes available Stress Graded**   Sizes in millimetres

on site using a linen or PVC reel tape measure. Remember to allow for the bearing on the internal walls. The thickness and depth of the joists is determined by the span (see Chapter 4 (p 56) for an example). This sort of detail will be on any set of drawings that have met with Building Regulations approval (refer to Approved Document A of the Building Regulations).

All sawn timber used in buildings should be treated with timber preservative. Timber is a food source for certain insects, and timber preservatives are designed to poison their food supply. A mixture of copper, chromium and arsenic (CCA) is forced into the wood under pressure; penetration is good. This type of chemical can be used on all timbers that are not intended to be decorated. If you need to decorate any treated timber you must specify an organic, spirit-based chemical such as Protim. CCA treatment is marginally cheaper per cubic metre. Handle treated timber with gloves.

*Stairs*
Remember to put this contract in hand. As soon as the chamber joists are in position you can invite joiners to look at the stairwell and estimates can be submitted.

*Roof Timbers*
The various members of a traditional roof are listed below (as opposed to a truss rafter roof which will be dealt with later) with their dimensions as a rough guide. These dimensions will on no account suit all roofs. Again the sizes should be detailed on the drawings.

|  | **Imperial** (*inches*) | **Metric** (*millimetres*) |
|---|---|---|
| Wall-plate | $4 \times 3$ | $100 \times 75$ |
| Rafters | $4 \times 2$ | $100 \times 50$ |
| Purlins | $9 \times 3$ | $225 \times 75$ |
| Ridge-board | $6 \times 1$ | $150 \times 25$ |
| Binders | $4 \times 2$ | $100 \times 50$ |
| Tile Battens | $1\frac{1}{2} \times \frac{3}{4}$ | $38 \times 19$ |
| Fascia-board | $6 \times 1$ (prepared) | $150 \times 25$ |
| Soffit | Plywood to suit the groove already machined in the back of the fascia | |

*Roof Tiles*
These are delivered to site ex works on pallets. Each standard tile measures 265mm × 165mm (10½in × 6½in); 1,000 tiles might weigh 1,120kg (22cwt). When laid on a roof to a gauge of 100mm (4in) you need sixty tiles to the square metre of roof. That square metre of roof will

weigh in the region of 68kg (12cwt per 100sq ft). In order to achieve a good mix of colour across the entire roof you should take tiles from all of the pallets throughout the job. Fix the tiles every fourth course with 38mm (1½in) 12 gauge aluminium alloy nails or a similar corrosion-resistant product. Some manufacturers will specify different nailing procedures and you should act in accordance with their recommendations. Do remember to consult the manufacturer's literature. Eave tiles (or 'under eaves') are fixed at the fascia and you will need six tiles per linear metre. They are 190mm × 165mm (7½in × 6½in).

Under-ridge tiles (or 'top course' tiles) measure 190mm × 165mm and are fixed at the ridge of the roof to complete the 'lap'.

'Tile and a half' tiles measure 265mm × 397mm (10½in × 16in) and are fixed on alternate courses at both ends of the roof to make the bond.

Ridge tiles are normally half round style and measure 299mm (12in) wide (internally) by 300mm (12in) long. There are much more splendid ridge tiles on the market, however, and it is well worth contacting your nearest roofing material wholesaler. Order your roof tiles as soon as you have passed the first floor joist stage. I have known tile companies to experience delays of six months. If you decide on a material, make sure you go into action. Always make enquiries about delivery dates: the building industry is subject to sudden famines.

### Electrical Requirements

An electrical wholesaler will advise you on every component you will need. The list is as follows:

> Double and single knock-out boxes (fixed before plastering)
> Shallow knock-out boxes to suit switches
> 2.5mm$^2$ two-core and earth cable (50m or 100m rolls)
> 1mm$^2$ two-core and earth cable (50m or 100m rolls)
> Short length of cooker cable (from consumer unit to cooker position)
> Short length of heat-resistant immersion heater cable (from immersion heater supply point to top of tank) earth wire
> Earth sheething, Oval conduit, Consumer unit
> Socket and switch face-plates. There are several different styles; ask to see the wholesaler's catalogues
> Pull switch for bathroom, Light fittings; pendent or batten holder,
> Clips to fix earth equipotential bonding, TV coaxial cable, Cable clips

### Plumbing Requirements

For central heating using a small-bore (not microbore) system you will need 15mm copper tubing together with either capillary or compression fittings, depending on which method of jointing you decide upon. The flow and return to the hot cylinder from the heat source should be 22mm copper tube. You will need to consider a circulation pump for the central heating system, together with a means of control, either a thermostat or a timer. For the domestic plumbing you will need 15mm copper tube plus fittings for hot and cold water supply downstairs and for cold supply upstairs, and for connecting the incoming mains to the roof tank. You will need 19mm copper tube to feed hot water to the bath from the hot cylinder. To connect up the waste pipes from all the sanitary ware you need to build a soil vent stack into which all the various pipes are connected. This terminates above the roof to ventilate the system. The main component of the stack is 100mm (4in) grey plastic pipe, which should be connected directly to each lavatory. The basin wastes are connected to the stack via 32mm (1¼in) plastic pipes and the bath and shower should have a 38mm (1½in) waste pipe. Radiators and radiator valves are described later.

### Rainwater goods

These are available from builders' merchants in four colours: white, cream, black and grey. You also have to choose between square section and half round. The half round is probably easier to work with.

### Flooring

Chipboard: ask for flooring grade chipboard (Type II) in 2440mm × 600mm (8ft × 2ft) sheets, tongued and grooved on four edges. British Standard 5669 covers this. Fix with annular nails. It comes in either 18mm (¾in) or 22mm (⅞in) thickness.

Tongued and grooved boards: these boards actually cover 115mm (4½in) when driven together. They are machined out of 120mm × 25mm (5in × 1in) sawn timber and should be ordered in running metres. Most prepared (planed) timber is supplied by the metre, not by the specific length as in sawn timber.

### Window boards (inside sills)

These are often made from Parana pine. The width can be either 225mm (9in) or 250mm (10in), machined from 32mm (1¼in) material (ex 32mm). They have a tongue on the leading edge which matches the groove in the bottom of the window frame.

### Loft Insulation

This comes in rolls, the width of which suits the spacings of the ceiling joists in the roof space. Each pack contains enough material to cover about 7.8m² (84sq ft) of ceiling, but the exact figure varies with different manufacturers. Most firms supply 80mm (3in) and 100mm (4in) thicknesses.

*Doors*

These should be the subject of a door schedule. The schedule should be set out as follows:

| Room | Number of doors | Dimensions (mm) | Description | Door furniture |
|---|---|---|---|---|
| Kitchen | 1 | 762 × 1,981 | (A) | Lever/latch |
| | 1 | External | (B) | Lever lock |
| | | 838 × 1,981 | | and 2 bolts |
| Sitting room | 2 | 762 × 1,981 | (C) | Lever/latch |

(A) Plywood lipped, 35mm (1⅜in) thick.
(B) Framed, ledged and braced, 44mm (1¾in) thick.
(C) Plywood lipped, 35mm (1⅜in) thick.

The width and height of a door is given here as 762mm × 1,981mm (2ft 6in × 6ft 6in), which represents the average. The specification of all doors must be sorted out at the design stage.

*Architrave, door stop and skirting board*

This needs to be ordered as a job lot, after obtaining three estimates from three different companies. It will be sold in running metres and it is available in several shapes and sizes. Generally, the more complicated the moulding, the harder it is to fix. Remember when ordering that internal doors require two sets of architrave, one each side of the opening.

*Sanitary Ware*

You have to know which type of lavatory you are intending to use from the early stages of building because the drainlayer, or yourself posing as the drainlayer, must know the exact distance from the wall at which the lavatory will be fixed, in order to correctly position the incoming 100mm (4in) drain. As this will be concreted into the oversite, it must be right.

Baths are more straightforward. Only the length varies, except in the case of the more outrageous shapes that are on the market.

I hope this list makes clear the necessity to build your house on paper before you start actually building. Delays caused by lack of materials are totally wasteful and damage the project more than any other management fault. Open an account with a builder's merchant. Find out what their range of stock is. Do not waste time asking advice about building methods from the man behind the counter. They are not craftsmen and they generally have a very limited knowledge of their products.

# 3
# LET'S BUILD

**Site Clearance and Setting Out**

Unless the site is a bare field, there will certainly have been some ancient structure occupying it, and most dwellings would have an access on to the highway. The first priority must be to establish an access point and a hard driveway on to the plot suitable to accommodate heavy lorries. A large portion of the plot will have to be devoted to the acceptance and storage of heavy building materials, and careful planning will ensure that the access does not become fatally blocked with piles of sand desperately unloaded from a mud-bound waggon. Any hardcore saved from buildings demolished can be used to form a base for the entrance. Pegs to mark the position of the access and driveway should make all this clear to the driver of the excavator. No demolition rubble may be used inside the new building and so the driveway may be a welcome use for the rubble.

The first job for the excavator, which in all cases will be a versatile JCB hired by the hour, is to cut the access between the pegs provided. The topsoil removed from the driveway may be stockpiled for future use. Plan this carefully: you must avoid heaps of soil in the wrong place. Mark everything on a rough sketch so that each part of the plot is allocated to different materials. From the moment the excavator rumbles on to the site and the long dreamed of day dawns – from that moment forth – the money starts to flow out. Your site begins to appreciate in value.

Make sure that all possible tidying and clearing has been done by hand in the weeks leading up to the day the excavator arrives. Hammer in four pegs to mark the rough outline of the building (house and garage). Proper preparations will ensure a successful day of digging. The machine may cost from £12 to £15 per hour, so do not waste time dithering over decisions. I suggest you have a list of events to show the driver:

Carve access
Dig driveway: push soil into heap as directed
Strip 150mm (6in) of soil from building position
Either: push soil into a heap, or load soil into trailers and dump.

Where possible push trees and bushes into a pile on the edge of the site for future burning. The top 150mm (6in) of soil over the area of the actual building must be removed (Building Regulations) as it may prove to be compressible under the huge weight of the building. Also, the organic matter may react with the building materials at a later date.

I think it is wise to strip the site, including the driveway and garage, and to stack the soil for future use. You can always haul it away if you have too much at the end. Your landscaping plans may change several times during the building process. Dig the access happy in the knowledge that you understand the highway authority's position. Although they are not obliged to visit the site, they will have been consulted at the planning stage and some decision will have been reached regarding your access, visibility, and all matters regarding traffic. It is your duty to find out the answers.

Excavate the entrance and driveway allowing for 150mm (6in) of hoggin or rubble plus a binding layer of finer materials to provide a surface at the end of the job. The base of the driveway will benefit from the passage of heavy vehicles during the building operation and should provide the makings of an excellent, level surface. You see already you are involved in fundamental decisions, with the finished level in mind. This is the terrifying truth about excavating: all decisions, depths of dig, levels, etc, have their bearing on the finished product, such as a drive that actually meets the blacktop – not one that overhangs it, or a kitchen floor that takes an escalator to reach from the garage. When you consider the conditions under which these fundamental levels are chosen, and the crude equipment often employed, it is a great wonder that so many buildings do in fact finish up in the correct field.

The man on the JCB will be used to working in confined, awkward spaces and he will perform feats of the most extraordinary deftness. The self-builder is ill at ease with noisy, expensive machinery; however, a great deal will be achieved. As I mentioned, do have a list of events for the day. You may feel foolish referring to your list, and you will almost certainly look foolish while the machine reduces your site to a wilderness of soil heaps, but in common with all subcontractors the digger driver will have his own picture of how your site should look – it will not resemble yours one bit.

On a commercial building site, the JCB would be on hire for several consecutive days: first to clear the site, then to follow on with excavating the foundations, service trenches and drains. This presupposes that the site foreman is present to 'set out' the building and to direct the careful digging of the trenches. I suggest that there is no great hurry at this very vital stage, and that you should send the JCB away after one day. You can now spend time 'setting out' the building in the earth. If you attempt to mark out the foundations with a £12 per hour monster at your elbow, I think your mind may wander. This stage of laying out the site needs quiet, deep thought. If you choose to employ a subcontract bricklaying gang then the setting out can be left to them. For our purposes I am going to assume that the self-builder wishes to grapple with this intensely satisfying task. Do not shrink from the science of setting out. It calls for lines and straight edges, in common with all building tasks. We need to achieve the following things: first, the buildings must be in the right place in relation to other established points; second, the corners must be right angles – if they are the building is said to be 'square', despite the fact that it may be L-shaped; third, the setting out must determine the various levels at which the ground floor, the garage floor, the damp-proof course and ultimately the ridge of the roof will finish.

The plans should by now have been securely mounted on a plywood board (the same dimensions as the unfolded plan) with the edges fixed with masking tape. The ground floor plan (1 : 50) and the site plan are both needed for setting out and could be mounted on either side of your board. Go to the corner of the site hut and select twenty-four 50mm × 50mm × 500mm (2in × 2in × 20in) pointed pegs. These will be used for corners and for the profile boards, whereas the stack of 300mm (12in) pegs will probably be used when determining levels. Fetch also the lump hammer and the skeins of building line, and the fifty-metre tape measure. From the site plan, which indicates clearly the position of the building in relation to either the highway, the boundary or another building, we can establish a corner. The ideal circumstance is where you have two measurements from one corner to two different fixed points. This will fix corner A (Figure 2). Another method is to take measurements from the highway or boundary to give you a parallel line as your front wall. This is called the base line and all other measurements can be taken from this. Hammer in a peg at each end and draw the line tight.

**Fig 2** Setting out diagrams showing how to form a square using the 3:4:5 method

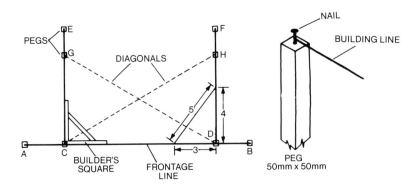

Site with profile boards in position

Leave the line in position. Check the distance between peg A and peg B. Now we need to create a right angle at these two corners and to do this we call on the theorem of Pythagoras, which states that the square of the length of the hypotenuse equals the sum of the squares of the other two sides.

This wonderful piece of geometry, when brought down to earth and the building site, becomes the 3 : 4 : 5 method of establishing a right angle. To apply this method we measure along the building line (base line) 3m and along the new line DF 4m; the remaining side of the right-angled triangle thus formed should be 5m. If it is not, your corner at D is not a right angle; you must adjust the line DF until the 5m measurement is dead on. A help in all this is to tie some thin white string in a knot at the point on the building line 3m from D and another knot at the 4m spot on DF.

Having measured out the side walls DH and CG, a further check can be made by measuring the diagonals DG and CH. These must be the same. If they are, the building is square, which means the four corners are right angles. When you have established the basic square, you can add pegs and lines to represent porches, wings and L-shapes.

The setting out continues by putting further information on to the

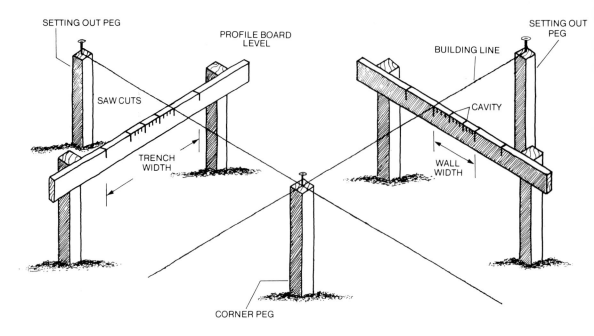

SETTING OUT PEG

PROFILE BOARD LEVEL

SETTING OUT PEG

BUILDING LINE

SAW CUTS

CAVITY

TRENCH WIDTH

WALL WIDTH

CORNER PEG

**Fig 3** Profile Boards in position providing permanent, accurate guides before digging the foundation trenches. Sand is sprinkled beneath each line to mark the outline of the trench

site, first for the excavator to read and then for the bricklayer to follow. The transmission of this information is done through profile boards. These temporary boards store all the marks and measurements to enable you to bring your building out of the ground and up to damp-proof course level. When you have established the lines marking the external walls, measure back 3m (10ft) from the corner and at each corner hammer in two pegs facing and straddling each line. To these pegs nail a stout board of perhaps 75mm × 25mm (3in × 1in). These profiles will be well back from the works and will not be disturbed by the excavator. The principle of the profile boards applies to many building tasks, allowing you to proceed gradually from broad inaccuracy to absolute accuracy while wrestling in difficult, often muddy conditions. So we have to determine the exact position of the foundation trenches within the site of the building which has been stripped of topsoil by the JCB and left reasonably flat. Using Figure 1, here is an example of setting up the profile boards for the line AB.

Drive a small roundheaded nail into the top of each corner peg (eg peg C). Pull a line tightly from peg B to peg A, noting the accuracy with which it passes over the nail head in peg C. Measure along the taut line in the direction of peg A, about 3m. Drive in the two profile pegs, which will support the profile board, either side of the line and sufficiently far apart to cover the total width of the foundation trench adequately (600mm). Nail the profile board to the pegs. The board wants to be 450mm (18in) from the ground and should be level. This is the first structure to be raised on your site. A taut line from A to B can now be raised over the profile board and a mark made to indicate the face of the external wall. Now repeat this process at each corner and where each cross wall adjoins the external walls. When you have constructed all the profiles and each profile has one mark on it indicating the external wall face, you can visit each profile and, using a pocket tape measure, mark the thickness of the external wall, followed by the cavity, followed by the internal wall. Then measure outwards from the external face of either wall to give you the outside marks for your foundation trenches. The profile boards now contain all the information of the setting out stage and they are standing back from the area of dig. Some cross walls may be built off the floor slab without separate foundations, but this depends on the load-bearing status and will be clearly indicated on the plan; they will also have been scrutinised by Building Regulation officials.

Permanently mark the profile boards by hammering in small nails at each point of interest. This serves both as a permanent weather-resistant mark and as a means of attaching the line when using the boards to mark out the trench position for the JCB. When all the profile boards are in position you can retire to the site hut, in the happy knowledge that important decisions have been made.

If you intend to hire the JCB for the foundation trenches immediately then you need some sand. It is too early to order the main bulk of your building sand – buy a few bags from the merchant. String up the lines from the profile boards using the nail heads that indicate the outside of the foundation trenches and sprinkle sand from a shovel exactly under the line.

**Foundation Trenches**

Do this both sides of the proposed trench. Do it on the day the JCB is to arrive so that rain does not erase the sand line. The JCB driver will work out the best order in which to dig the trenches. The soil that you dig can either be loaded into a trailer and hauled away from the site altogether, or loaded into the trailer and dumped on a suitable part of the site for future use or removal. The subsoil from the trenches is without value unless you wish to raise up a part of the site. If possible hire a tractor and trailer and drive it yourself. Leave some subsoil for backfilling around the foundations on the outside of the building. The building inspector will not allow any soil backfill inside the building.

As the JCB is digging the trenches it is vital that you check the depth of dig as you go. To do this we need to establish a fixed point, either in relation to a nearby known level such as a manhole cover in the road or in relation to ground level at its highest point on the site. At the corner on the highest part of the site drive in a peg to 150mm (6in) above ground level. At each of the other corners drive in a peg to the same level. Cut a batten 1m in length to check the depth of the trench below the level of the damp-proof course. If the site is level you simply measure, with a pocket tape, from ground level to the trench bottom. Too much depth will cost you dearly in concrete.

The excavation will probably take a day. By the end of it you will feel soundly committed to your project and satisfied that the hours of planning and worrying, about the setting out, about the position of the building and the accuracy of your calculations are stamped with muddy approval. The trenches must now be checked by calling on the profile boards to release, once more, their secrets. Some trenches may have to be straightened or tidied by hand and the bottoms made firm with a shovel. The building inspector will wish to see the empty trenches, with special emphasis on depth. If all goes well and your trench bottoms are nice and firm he will accept the depth of dig. This is normally between 800mm (2ft 8in) and 1m (3ft 3in) so I think it is wise to allow in your cost calculations for a one-metre dig. A trial hole in one corner of the site may indicate the conditions you will face and will alert you to any unusual seams of soft material which would call for deep foundations. In some extreme positions where the site is near a river or overlying some soft sand the weight of the building may have to be carried on a raft of concrete. This is a specialised job and should really be tackled by an architect who has met the problem before.

The building inspector must be made to feel welcome and it is important that he is your friend. He will not give, within his brief, advice or opinions as to how to overcome snags, but he will be supportive, and he will at all times tell you the standards required by his authority. Generally it will be one of his more interesting site visits; he will quickly realise that you are building to the highest standards, and no doubt this will be a relief from housing estates, public lavatories and bus shelters.

He is in close contact with the local building infrastructure and will have a vast knowledge of local conditions. You can very often invite him to explain baffling technical problems over a cup of tea in the site hut.

When you have carried out your fine adjustments to the trenches and the building inspector, awash with tea, vanishes, you are at liberty to have a day off, or to fill your trenches with 'approved' concrete. It is essential not to leave the trenches for too long. Stray animals and 'unapproved' humans may wander into them (insurance cover is essential) and rain may cause them swiftly to collapse. It is ideal to concrete the day after the visit by the inspector.

## Concrete Foundations

(Turn to Chapter 2 for an example of how to calculate quantities of concrete required.)

The first job is to drive metal pegs into the base of the foundation trenches to indicate the depth of the concrete. The requirement will be a minimum of 450mm (18in) and the width of the trench (600mm, 24in) must be filled. Having agreed this depth measurement with the building inspector you simply drive a peg in one corner and, using a straight board, transfer the level to the next peg two metres away. There is another method using a Cowley level, which can be hired from your nearest tool hire shop. This is a marvellous levelling device which is accurate enough for a house builder and can easily be understood by a self-builder. I shall dwell on this gadget as it answers the fears raised by levels and may prevent a few sleepless nights.

As you look through the instrument your line of sight strikes the staff and the crossbar. Your assistant (yes, you need a friend for two hours)

**Fig 4** Sketch to show a cowley level in operation

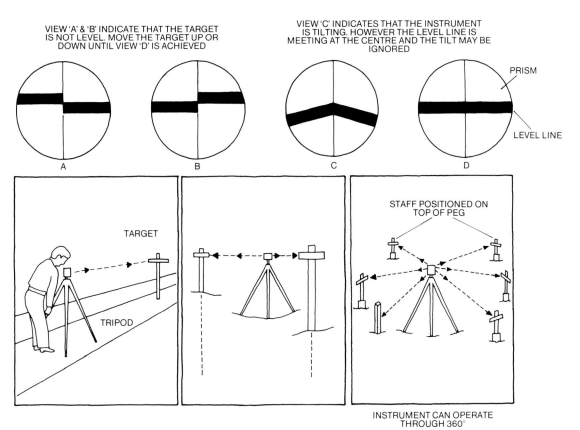

VIEW 'A' & 'B' INDICATE THAT THE TARGET IS NOT LEVEL. MOVE THE TARGET UP OR DOWN UNTIL VIEW 'D' IS ACHIEVED

VIEW 'C' INDICATES THAT THE INSTRUMENT IS TILTING. HOWEVER THE LEVEL LINE IS MEETING AT THE CENTRE AND THE TILT MAY BE IGNORED

PRISM

LEVEL LINE

A          B          C          D

TARGET

TRIPOD

STAFF POSITIONED ON TOP OF PEG

INSTRUMENT CAN OPERATE THROUGH 360°

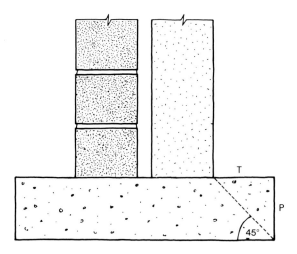

**Fig 5** Illustrates the minimum width and depth of the foundation in relation to a cavity wall. 'T' must at least equal 'P'.

must raise or lower the crossbar until you see both halves of the crossbar as one complete line. The foot of the staff should be placed on the first peg (which will be driven in to 450mm (18in) above trench bottom) and adjustments made to the crossbar. The staff must be held vertically. Now if your assistant progresses to the next peg (two metres down the trench, because although the board is absent two metres is a good distance when laying the concrete as regards keeping it level) in order to read the same level, because the crossbar will only be in one line in one exact place, he or she must adjust the peg downwards until this is achieved. Then to the next peg and so on until the whole foundation is pegged out.

You can see how this Cowley level could be used to determine the damp-proof course level, which is to be no less than 150mm (6in) above ground level at the highest point on the site. It follows that at the lowest corner it will be considerably more than 150mm. Simply place the tripod in the middle of the site. Place the staff tip on the datum peg, be it an arbitrary peg 150mm above ground level or a manhole in the street, and transfer that level to other pegs at each of the four corners of the building. All levels on the plan will be related to the datum point. I stress that you may have established your own datum in relation to existing ground level. Imagine the datum peg as a tiny ledge from which measurements of height and depth can be made. For the purposes of considering foundation trench concrete, the datum peg was 150mm (6in) above ground level and we fixed our staff and crossbar at that point. Reading that level, we could transfer the level to the trench via a long batten whose height was set level with the datum. We could then measure down this batten to determine the top of the concrete.

So if the depth of dig was one metre from ground level (1,150mm from damp-proof course level) then we could measure down the batten 700mm and make a mark. This would be the top of the concrete. Drive a peg into this mark and level all other pegs to it. Try to hammer the pegs in straight. In stony conditions use an iron fencing bar to start the hole. When you are happy that all the pegs are at exactly the same level you are ready for concreting.

Readymix or truck-mixed concrete from your nearest bulk mixing plant is the most efficient way of doing the job. The reasons for and against readymix are listed here:

> For:     Thorough mix throughout batch
>            No need to store large quantities of ballast and cement
>            Much quicker
>            Easily finished in one day.
> Against: More expensive per cubic metre.

The expense of readymix is cancelled out by convenience and speed for the self-builder, bearing in mind that the weather is uncertain. It is an urgent matter to get the building out of the ground.

Order the correct amount of concrete to arrive at a certain time and to be of an approved mix to suit foundations. A normal mix would be 1 : 8 (one part of cement to eight parts of all-in ballast). The truck simply drives on to the site, as near to the trenches as he can manage. Ask the driver how wet the material is. If concrete is too wet it will be easily worked and moved about but it will be weak because the smaller particles separate from the larger during the mixing process. The driver should be experienced in adding the correct amount of water. Generally, the drier the mix, the stronger it will be. As a matter of interest, the wetness of a concrete mix is described by the cement to water ratio. An average ratio is 0.60, which translated means 50kg of cement (one bag) mixed with 30 litres of water. This is influenced greatly by the moisture content of the aggregate, but as far as your house is concerned you can leave it to the readymix truck driver. You do not want to get a reputation on the building grape-vine as a fuss-pot. Keep the concrete damp for seven days after laying.

If the readymix truck cannot get near enough to some of the trenches then you will have to barrow the concrete across planks to the far flung bits of trench. The concrete is laid with a shovel using the peg tops as a guide to depth; the back of the shovel provides an adequate finish. The building inspector may wish to be present at the 'pouring'.

*The Mixer*

Here is a quick lesson in on-site machine mixing. If you choose to mix your own concrete out of some sense of devotion to duty, this section may be of help. Let us tackle the question first of all, of whether to hire a mixer or to buy one. The size of machine needs to be a 4 : 3 petrol-driven mixer mounted on a stand. This is quite adequate for mixing all mortar and, if need be, all concrete. This type of machine will cost £14 per week to hire. If it is hired for six months then you can expect a discount of thirty per cent.

$$
\begin{array}{ll}
\text{24 weeks @ £14 per week} & = \text{£336.00} \\
\text{Less discount of 30 per cent} = & \underline{\phantom{0}100.80} \\
& \text{£235.20 excl VAT}
\end{array}
$$

If you purchase a new machine it will cost £185, a saving of £50 compared with hiring. You own the machine and may use it for as long as the building job lasts, at the end of which you could sell it.

Always start the mixer before filling the drum. The drum should be loaded with half the aggregate, gauged by bucket, followed by one bucket of cement, followed by the remainder of the aggregate. A shovel is a very inaccurate method of gauging and if you are to achieve a uniform mix of the correct ratio of cement to aggregate (1 : 8), I suggest that a bucket or box is used. Mix the concrete for two minutes, dry, then add the water slowly and allow to mix for a further two minutes to ensure adequate distribution of the fine particles. All-in aggregate consists of particle sizes ranging from 4.7mm (³⁄₁₆in) to 38mm (1½in) in diameter. You must position your mixer so that the drum throws the mixture over. You can easily see this and adjust the wheels accordingly. If you do not, the mix will simply pack on to the back of the drum and no mixing of ingredients will occur. When you have finished mixing, throw half a dozen half-bricks or stones into the drum with a bucket full of water to clean the paddles and drum. Turn this out and switch off. Shovel away the 'cleanings', otherwise they will soon become a mountain.

## Masonry to Damp-Proof Course

As soon as possible after the drama of concreting the foundations, you must 'bring the building out of the ground'. The longer the trenches are open to the elements, the more likely you are to experience landslides. From the flat, level concrete we must bring the external and internal walls up to damp-proof course level. You may wish to include the garage: if it is an integral part of the house then you must bring it up together with the main house. If the garage is a separate building it is still

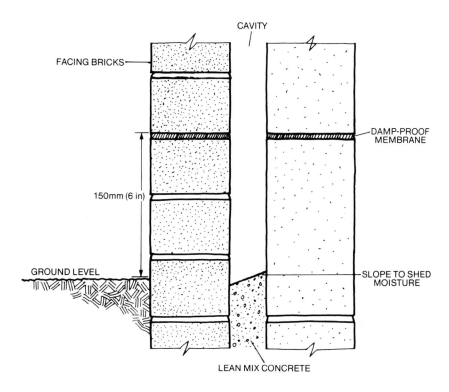

CAVITY

FACING BRICKS

150mm (6 in)

GROUND LEVEL

DAMP-PROOF MEMBRANE

SLOPE TO SHED MOISTURE

LEAN MIX CONCRETE

**Fig 6** Showing the position of the damp course on outer and inner leaf. Note that the cavity is filled up to ground level

wise to bring it up to concrete slab level (DPC plus concrete subfloor) as this enables you to back-fill the trenches and tidy the site.

A damp-proof course is a barrier designed to prevent the ground moisture from travelling up the porous brick walls and causing damage to the internal plaster and decorations. Most buildings erected since 1945 contain a damp-proof course and are constructed with a cavity between outer and inner skin. A damp-proof course must also be provided wherever the cavity is bridged, which is the case at all window and door openings. At this stage we shall consider the horizontal barrier of the outer and inner walls. As we have said, the Building Regulations demand that the damp-proof course is not less than 150mm (6in) above ground level. This ensures that the damp-proof membrane is not bridged and rendered useless. To start this phase we need enough concrete blocks and facing bricks to raise the walls the correct number of courses to DPC level. The most efficient system is to calculate the quantities of blocks and bricks needed for the whole building and have them all delivered. The calculations are in Chapter 2.

It is likely that the foundations will be deep enough to take two courses of 18 × 9 × 4 concrete blocks to reach DPC level. Where the outer wall breaks through the ground you must change rapidly to facing brickwork. Nothing is worse than concrete blocks 'grinning' above the soil line; it is better by far to bury a course of facing bricks. We must remember to allow for service ducts to come into the building between the top of the concrete footing and damp-proof course.

The view from your site hut resembles an unfinished archaeological dig. No one problem is absolutely solved. It is frightening to consider the sheer physical work that lies ahead. How are you going to move concrete blocks across the site? Every builder fears this part of the operation. The weather is more critical now than at any other time.

Launch forth from the site hut with a trowel, the building lines, a bucket containing hammer and bolster, and a spirit level and make for the nearest corner to the mixer. Sweep off the concrete footings and reinstate the lines on the profile boards. We need a pile of concrete blocks at each corner, within easy reach of the trench but not in danger of causing a landslide. We need a spot board, which will become our closest friend. You must have a light, mobile table from which to scoop mortar on its way to the wall. This is the spot board, and it consists of a piece of plywood measuring 450mm (18in) square by 25mm (1in) thick, supported on four bricks or blocks and placed as near as possible to the work. When you are building a long wall it is wise to position a spot board every two metres along the length. Time spent on the layout of your site will bring real satisfaction to the tasks performed. Building is concerned, always, with moving and arranging vast quantities of heavy, lifeless materials. The only way to make this swift and enjoyable with the minimum strain is to spend time carefully laying out each section before attacking it.

While you are arranging the blocks and collecting your thoughts, the mixer can be running with a 4 : 1 building sand to cement mix, together with a capful of mortar plasticiser (Febmix or Cemplas). This serves to make the mortar more workable, more buttery, so that it will roll into a sausage on the trowel and will leave the trowel cleanly.

Take the spirit level and plumb down from the taut building line A (see Figure 7) to the foundation concrete on which you have placed a thin smear of mortar. Make a mark against the bottom of the level. This has effectively transferred the mark of the outside of the outside wall into a physical mark on the footing. Do this again one metre up line A (from the corner) and join the two marks in the mortar smear using the spirit level as a straight edge. Now repeat this plumbing down process on line B. Measure 11in from these marks in the mortar and construct a series of lines forming the inner margin of the inner skin. Eleven inches represents 4in for the outer wall, 2in for the cavity and 4in for the inner

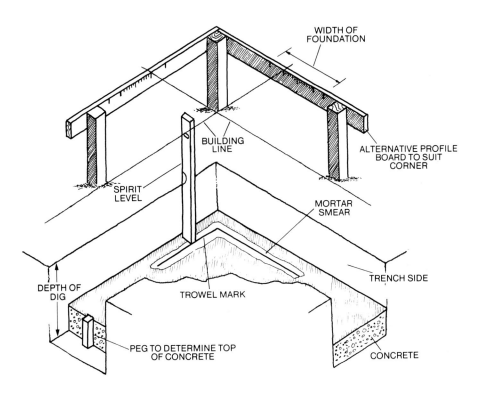

**Fig 7** To transfer the marks on the profile board onto the surface of the foundation concrete

wall, with a tolerance of 1in to allow for metric blocks. The metric equivalent looks like this: 115mm, plus 50mm, plus 115mm. For our purposes, we are determined to use 150mm (6in) internal blocks for the inner skin in order to raise the thermal efficiency of the building. This is discussed in the section on insulation requirements (p 15).

So now we have a corner on which we can build the blockwork of both walls up to damp-proof course height in one operation, racking back at each corner (see p 57). When all the corners are up and racked back then you can fill in the lengths of the walls using a building line, with building pins at either end pushed into the mortar one joint behind the last block laid. This line will give you the height and straightness of each course. Slowly, the distance between the corners will be filled in and with immense relief you reach DPC level. Meanwhile, the two leaves of walling have to be tied together as work proceeds so that they stand as one mass, despite their hollow, secret cavity. The types of wall tie available are illustrated (in Figure 8) and I recommend for empty cavities (ie those not filled with insulating material) the butterfly wall tie. The wall tie must be positioned with the twisted centre portion facing downwards

Transferring the information stored on the profile board to the foundation concrete

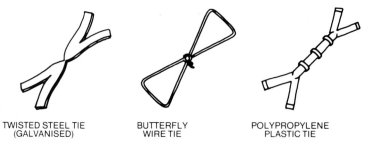

| TWISTED STEEL TIE (GALVANISED) | BUTTERFLY WIRE TIE | POLYPROPYLENE PLASTIC TIE |

**Fig 8** Three types of wall tie on the market

to allow water to drip off before passing into the inner skin. Butterfly wall ties have better sound insulation properties. The ties must be built into the masonry at 900mm (3ft) intervals along the course and every six courses of brickwork or the equivalent blockwork. The inner skin coursing must therefore match the outer skin to enable the wall ties to lie flat. Wall ties have to be used throughout the building from the foundations to the wall-plate. Wherever a drain or duct passes into the building you must bridge it with a small concrete lintel.

When the building looks like a hollow box half-buried in the ground with all walls level and all cavities present, spanned at intervals with wall ties, and all corners beautifully square, the profile boards can be dismantled and that phase of the job is over.

The main reason for tackling the brickwork up to DPC level before dealing with the drains is because all drains are ultimately measured off inside walls and so it makes sense to establish the exact positions of the inner skin first. We are now DPC-high, but there is no need to actually fix the damp-proof membrane until we continue the brickwork.

Of the two next tasks to be tackled (ie the drains and the concrete subfloor), I would deal with the drains first and fill the site and pour the concrete subfloor as a treat for completing the grizzly drains.

## Drains

The purpose of drains is to convey foul materials from all points of the building wherein such things originate, swiftly and without snags, to the main sewer in the street if you are lucky enough to have one, or if not, to a septic tank or cesspool built by you within the site at the correct safe

Close up of trowel marks on the foundation concrete. The line in the mortar smear is plumbed down from the building line

distance from the house. Rain water must be dealt with in a similar way, either to a storm water drain running adjacent to the sewer, or into a soakaway, the correct safe distance from the building. The drain-building task is not one to be feared and is well within the capability of the eager self-builder. To build a drain system that works and that carries local authority approval is a worthy addition to your curriculum vitae and better equips you for life.

The drain runs need to pass out of the building underground and should be spanned by a lintel in each wall to protect the pipe should the building subsequently settle. From the building the drain should slope at a fall of 1 : 40 (that is a drop of 1m in every 40m of distance travelled). This gradient is vital as too steep a fall would result in the solid matter separating from the liquids, while too shallow a gradient would not

**Fig 9** Diagram of glass fibre septic tank on a concrete base

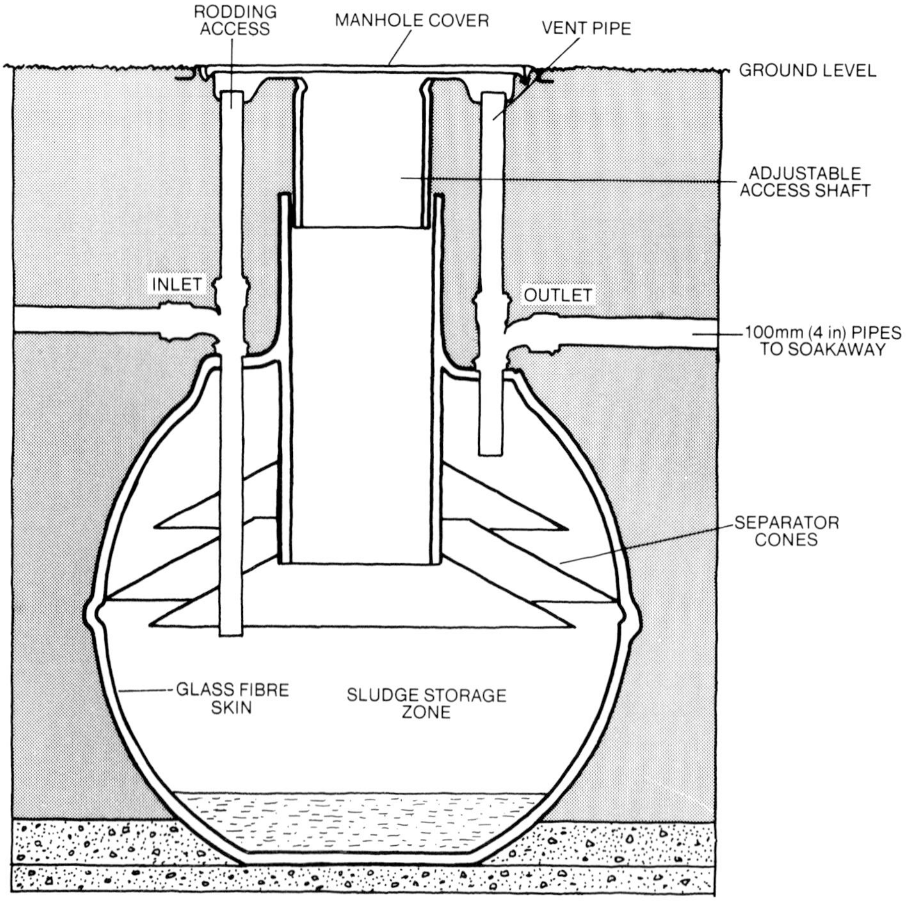

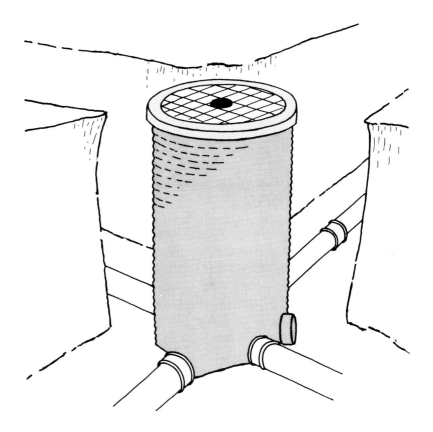

**Fig 10** Showing details of a plastic manhole

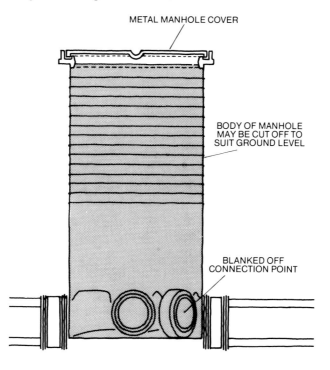

METAL MANHOLE COVER

BODY OF MANHOLE
MAY BE CUT OFF TO
SUIT GROUND LEVEL

BLANKED OFF
CONNECTION POINT

Site before filling the area enclosed by the internal walls. The water main is carried in a duct

provide sufficient flow to carry the solids down the length of drain.

Having decided on a position for the cesspool in a quiet, forgotten corner of the garden, drain excavation starts at the building end and at a steady 1 : 40 gradient arrives at the cesspool at a certain distance below ground level. This needs to be as shallow as possible to avoid the huge costs of excavating deeply for the cesspool. On the route from the house to the cesspool any change in direction has to incorporate a manhole to enable the lucky householder, in this case you, to rod the drains effectively. Drain rods do not cohabit with corners. When designing a drain layout make sure that everything is as straight as possible.

I suggest a JCB should be hired for a day, together with tractor and trailer, and that you launch into the drainage business with gusto, endeavouring to dig not only the drain trenches but also the hole into which will fit the cesspool of your choice.

Once again, the drain runs should be marked by stretching a building

(*Opposite above*) View of site before 'fill' showing load bearing walls taken down to foundation level

(*Opposite below*) 100mm Drains connected up

line from a peg at the point of exit from the house to the first manhole (change of direction) and thence to the cesspool. Sprinkle building sand beneath the line to indicate clearly to the driver his plan of attack.

The JCB driver can be used as the 'staff' man when shooting levels with the Cowley level. He can dig by eye so far and then a check can be made as to the gradient of the trench bottom.

The pipes should be laid on pea gravel, which will have to be levelled to the tops of pegs much like the concrete was in the foundation trenches. The purpose of the pea gravel is to provide a snug bed for the pipes while not holding them in a rigid line. Any subsequent movement can be absorbed by the bed and by the pipes via their flexible coupling (see Figure 11).

There are several underground drainage systems available. Of all of them I think two should be considered with a view to self-assembly. There are the 100mm plastic pipes which come in long lengths and which simply push together, or there is a clay system made by Hepsleeve which provides satisfying 100mm pipes in 1500mm lengths, together with rubber joiners that, with gentle persuasion, will push together. I favour the clay system and it works out marginally cheaper than the plastic equivalent.

The method of laying the Hepsleeve is simple. Once the trenches are dug and the manhole squares are excavated to allow the brickwork to commence, and once the pea gravel is laid to the appropriate level, you drive in a peg in the centre of the trench at both ends. Draw a line tight and begin to place the pipes to the line. The first pipe nestles against the end peg and should be fitted with its collar. It may be possible to connect a 90° bend on to the first pipe before you start: any connecting work that can be accomplished on terra firma saves a struggle later. However you approach this first section, it must end up in a firm position to allow you to push hard against it with the next pipe. Assuming all is straight with the line and all is level with the world, and it is not raining, you can offer up the next length of pipe suitably smeared with connecting lubricant (or washing-up liquid) and press it against the first collar. Take a garden fork and push the tines down into the base of the trench, all the while touching the end of the pipe plus coupler. Now lever the pipe gently forwards into the first coupler until the joint is fully made.

Be careful not to wade about like a buffalo in your level pea gravel, and be sure to keep the pipes true to the line. I suggest when this is done you might lay the foundation slab of each manhole. This may be done using a

(*Opposite above*) P.V.C. drainage showing small access manhole and two rodding points

(*Opposite below*) Large P.V.C. manhole in position. The height will be adjusted to suit ground level

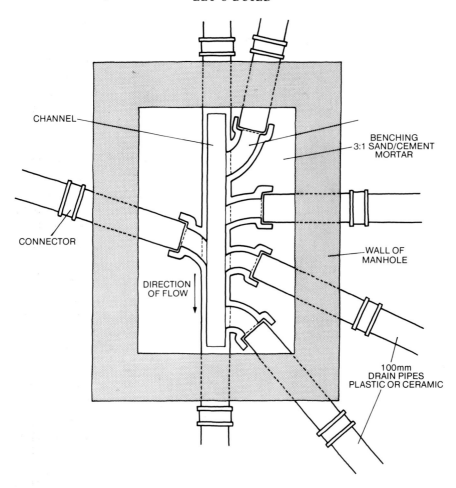

CHANNEL

BENCHING
3:1 SAND/CEMENT
MORTAR

CONNECTOR

WALL OF
MANHOLE

DIRECTION
OF FLOW

100mm
DRAIN PIPES
PLASTIC OR CERAMIC

**Fig 11** Diagram of layout of manhole showing the channel in position

100mm high framework like a small box, placed in the hole and the concrete level screeded off at the rim of the box.

The size of the standard manhole (457mm × 610mm internal) allows rodding access and that is about all. The manhole cover is 18in × 24in and should fit nicely on to the walls of the manhole. You can use pre-formed concrete sections, which are quicker but not quite so satisfying.

When you have constructed the manhole, either in brickwork using calcium silicate bricks or with the interlocking concrete sections, you can add the base channel, which is a pipe cut in half, to the base concrete. This connects both inlet and outlet of the manhole, and therefore must be positioned abutting both pipes. The concrete can then be built up around the channel to provide a corridor for the sewage to flow through. The walls of this corridor must finish level with the tops of the inlet and outlet pipes and the walls must be capped with a screed of 2 : 1 sand to cement mortar and trowelled smooth. The entire manhole has to be rendered externally to provide a smooth clean surface, to prevent the flow of ground water from the surrounding soil. It is better to complete the laying of the channel and the benching around it after you have laid three courses of bricks, simply to give you more room to work. Then you can finish the walls up to ground level, ready to receive the manhole cover. The manhole cover in domestic surroundings can be either thin ugly metal or smooth stone-coloured concrete which quickly fades into the environment. Unless the manhole is going to withstand vehicles it can be 'pedestrian' in strength. Bed on the covers and frames after the building inspector has tested the drains. Before sending in the relevant building card make sure that the drains terminate inside the house with appropriate bends. Make sure that all joints are pushed up tight and that the pipes are straight. Make sure that the benching in each manhole is neat and smooth, and that the joint between pipe and manhole is sufficiently cemented up. All this creates a sense of thoroughness. You should hire or buy two drain plugs which the inspector may use; he may air test the system to find any leaks or cracks. If the air pressure does not hold on a given section of pipework then you must fill that part with water against a drain plug at the lower end and find the leak, and hence the fault.

The septic tank will arrive on a lorry and can be manhandled or lifted by the JCB into the hole dug for the purpose. The manufacturer's instructions vary but Figure 9 illustrates the basic task quite adequately. If you are working in a high water table then the tank must be filled with water to 'sink' it to the required depth; once secured with concrete the water is pumped out of the tank. Very good motor-driven pumps can be hired by the day. Remember that all sorts of civil engineering problems can be solved by the self-builder, lonely as it may sound. Do not despair.

When you have passed the test, apart from serious celebrations in the site hut, you can back-fill all your trenches and tidy the site.

## Services

All three services may be provided underground if you are lucky. First approach the local electricity supply company and obtain a quotation for providing power to your house. Do the same with British Telecom and with the water authority. In all cases meet their representatives on site to discuss the method of provision. If it is to be underground, and let us hope that it is, find out what method of ducting is needed. The water authority insists on a sound duct 100mm in diameter to be laid at a minimum depth of 750mm; through this duct you must pass the alkathene flexible pipe. The object of the duct, which can be 100mm

Blake's corner profile in position. Spotboard in the foreground

plastic underground drainpipe, is to protect the pipe and to allow it to be withdrawn at a later date should any leaks occur. You only need a duct under the building, and it is normal to aim the water pipe at the kitchen sink or the wash-house; so wherever it passes under the building it must be ducted. Elsewhere on the site the pipe may be buried in a trench 750mm (30in) deep with a covering of sand over and around it to protect it from sharp stones.

From the water main in the road it is normal to have a water authority stop valve in a special inaccessible box and for the site to be provided with water for building via self-installed length of alkathene pipe plus stop valve, which can be directed to a point near the mixer and fixed to a fence post. The water main into the house can remain dead with its end clearly marked at the end of the trench, its open end covered in some way to stop soil from blocking it.

British Telecom will provide an armoured cable which can be buried in the same trench as the water pipe, provided the direction of supply is the same. This must be ducted in the same way into and around the building.

Exactly the same considerations apply to the electric power. You will need a temporary supply to run kettles, drills, toasters, radios and power saws and, one day, lights, so it is essential to provide a position in the site hut for a power supply, the exact nature of which will be thrashed out with the power company's representative. You may wish to install the house meter box in its final position and run your temporary supply from this point (see page 146–8).

If you are fortunate enough to have a gas supply available then the local gas board office will advise you on how to secure a supply to your house. In the case of the public sewer, which you will have to connect to, make sure you contact the local authority and meet the representative on site. Leave plenty of time to sort out the provision of all services.

# 4
# CONSTRUCTION OF WALLS

## Concrete Subfloor

In my experience the building inspector calls at a self-build site almost on a daily basis just to satisfy his curiosity and to rest easy at night. As soon as he has passed the brickwork up to DPC level, and once the mortar has set, you can begin to 'fill' the site. This means bringing the level up from the foundation trenches on the inside to 125mm (5in) below DPC level with clean, washed stone. The Building Regulations covering this aspect of the work firmly forbid poor-quality hardcore. Our local gravel pit produces a commodity called 'rejects'; these are clean stones, rejected from some other part of their daily production, but quite suitable for filling voids inside a building. The site was stripped of topsoil, remember, and so the uneven bomb-site appearance within the walls must be raised to an orderly, level pool of stone which will in time receive a 100mm (4in) layer of concrete known as the 'oversite'.

Now the 'fill' is delivered in a ten-ton capacity tipping lorry. The calculations for the quantities of stone required are given in Chapter 2. This lorry will reverse as near as possible to the low walls of the house, and if all things are in your favour the stones may be deposited in heaps over the walls. If the ground conditions or the weather are against you, as is usually the case in Britain, then the forlorn Chesil Bank must be barrowed laboriously over a complex of scaffold plank runways into the interior. Farmers possess most sophisticated mechanical shovels and you may persuade a neighbour to shift your pile of stones one Saturday morning in exchange for some strong ale.

With the stone spread evenly and finishing below DPC level we can now cover it with a layer of building sand. This serves to fill the voids and provides an even surface on which to lay the damp-proof membrane in the form of a polythene sheet. The sheet is sold in rolls 2m (6ft) wide and 50m long and has other uses besides that of the damp-proof membrane. Overlap the sheet where a join is necessary. The sheet must pass up the brickwork to reach the damp-proof membrane on the inner skin, so that the oversite concrete sits in a shallow polythene bag. The sheet can be trimmed with a Stanley knife after the concrete has set.

Blake's profile. Oversite concrete. Brickwork 'Racked Back'

**Fig 12** To show a cross section through cavity wall together with site fill (hardcore)

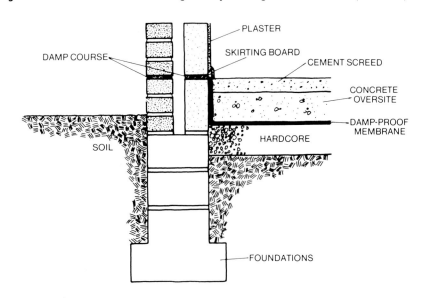

Lay out the polythene sheet on the day you hope to lay the concrete. Have you provided ducts for all services that traverse the oversite? Again I think readymix is the most efficient method, for all the reasons stated in the section on foundations (p 20). The readymix lorry will manoeuvre as near as possible to the building, but it will be necessary to barrow a fair amount of concrete into position. Divide the areas to be concreted into bays using 100mm × 50mm (4in × 2in) timber of not more than 2m in width. You cannot screed off concrete in wide bays because of the weight of material involved; and it is sufficient to concrete a bay and leave a 2m gap and then fill the next bay. When both these first bays are dry you can return and concrete the gaps using the dry concrete as levels from which to work. It is vital to get the 100mm × 50mm guides absolutely level. You may find it necessary to pack the timber in places to obtain a level. Remember there is only a sand and cement screed to go on top of the oversite concrete. This will not hide mistakes.

The laying of the concrete is achieved by emptying it from the barrow, then roughly levelling with a shovel and finally passing a straight board over the guides, using a sawing action. Remove the surplus that builds up in front of the board and marvel at the smoothness of concrete behind the board. Avoid puncturing the polythene sheet with the wheelbarrow. As you move across the building, each guide can be prised out of the fresh concrete and used in a new position, and the narrow channel thus formed can be filled in and tamped level.

Suddenly there are smooth, hard, flat surfaces appearing out of the chaos of mud and trenches. The ends of the drains and the service ducts are held firmly in concrete. The room sizes become apparent. You are surprised at the proportions and rush to the plans. Can this be so small?

If you have decided on a suspended ground floor, as was the case with Hancocks, then the same oversite procedure applies, but the finished level of concrete may be level with the ground level outside; it must not finish below ground level. The suspended floor is then built off the oversite, honeycomb brick walls bearing the timber flooring that will finish at DPC level, or just above. This feature will be explained in Chapter 8.

The arguments for and against solid floors polarise, boringly, around money. Costs weigh heavily in favour of solid floors, although we may favour suspended floors: they elevate your ground floor above the cold earth; they provide a springy platform to walk on and to stand on, particularly in front of the kitchen sink; they provide a softer landing for a falling child or a fainting aunt. Finally, from the quality point of view,

(*Opposite above*) Close up of Blake's profile in use

(*Opposite below*) Raising the line after each course. The profile is plumbed up once only in both directions

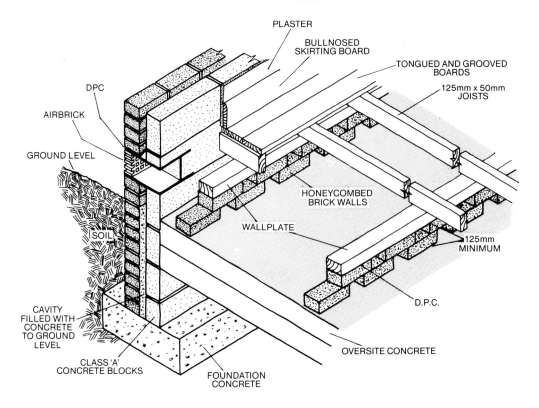

**Fig 13** Suspended timber floor with ventilation and honeycomb brick 'sleeper' walls

which must be ever present in the thinking of the self-builder, it is simply more satisfying to live upon a wooden floor than a concrete one.

While the concrete oversite cures it should be out of bounds for two days. You can spend a few happy hours in the site hut checking through the materials needed for the next phase.

## Walls from DPC to First Floor Joists

As we have some time on our hands, I am going to explain the preparation of window frames and external door frames, and the general marshalling of materials and equipment to raise the building up easily and swiftly to accept the first floor.

Window frames have been decided upon at the planning stage and should have been ordered in week one (see Chapter 2). There are such a variety of joinery firms producing 'standard' windows that a local one may suit and will probably be quicker on delivery. If you are interested in the proportions of the windows then you will be disappointed by the 'standard' approach to fenestration. The reason why Georgian windows are so excellent and so easy on the eye is that the architect pursued the

60

'golden section' and proportioned the window in accordance with that law. Joinery manufacturers however (and it is an interesting use of words to link 'joinery' with 'manufacturer') pay no heed to the golden section. They ignore the sizes and dictates of brickwork, which has to follow a strict, vertical pattern with 'course' heights exactly related to window heights.

However, to have windows specially made for your building may be far too costly, so I shall assume that your site hut is surrounded by 'standard' mass-produced softwood windows, stacked in the approved manner and covered in a polythene sheet. The windows should be stacked vertically with their sills resting on timber rails. The window frames and opening lights will have been primed at the factory if requested, or left unprimed if you wish to stain them rather than paint them.

The first job is to cut off the 'horns' on both window head and sill. Make a pencil mark with a carpenter's square and saw cleanly and precisely, leaving the window frame ready to be built in without obstructions. The purpose of the horn is to strengthen the window in transit and

View of plastic manhole with 90° connection from house. The overall height can be adjusted. The light coloured stone is pea shingle

View of 100mm drain pipe terminating inside the building together with a 100mm connection to receive rainwater on the outside, as near to the corner as possible. Notice the concrete lintel carrying the wall over the drain

to keep it 'square', and also in some circumstances to permit the corner to be built into the brickwork. The cut ends should be brush treated with suitable timber preservative. This spot treatment with preservative typifies the detail and care which the self-builder can exercise on his own site. Short cuts are not the answer. Quality and job satisfaction lie down the road of 'spot treatments' and meticulous detail. Separate the ground floor windows from the first floor and mark them room by room. We can treat the external door frames in the same manner, remembering not to remove the timber bracing until the frames are soundly built in. The same spot treatment applies. Now rummage in the site hut for the frame cramps which were ordered with the DPC and put them in a plastic bucket, together with the correct number of the zinc-coated wood screws (one inch, number eights).

Check on cavity wall ties, petrol for the mixer, cement from the cement store, febmix, building line and pins, spot board and tools. Go forth on to the site and begin to load the concrete slab, along all external walls, with internal blocks to form the inner skin of the cavity. These piles need to be a sensible height and two feet in from the inner skin will allow you to work in comfort. In between each pile place a spot board on two blocks. I continue to stress the need to approach these stages with the utmost precision. If you do not, your site will deteriorate into a mindless muddle with broken bricks to trip over, holes to fall down and nothing to hand when you need it. Building sites are medieval compared with other industries, even agriculture, so at least ensure it is tidy medieval.

Repeat the loading out process on the outside of the building using facing bricks, taking the same care with positioning and ergonomic considerations. Level the ground first before building a stack of bricks. Consider also that you will need some form of early scaffolding supported on trestles. You cannot lay bricks unless you are absolutely comfortable.

Now we can mix a small batch of mortar at 5 : 1 strength in order to bed on the damp-proof membrane, the rolls of which are stacked in the site hut. Turn the mix into a barrow and use the mortar straight from the barrow, as you will travel quickly round the building with this job. Spread a thin layer of mortar on to inner and outer skins and press the

**Fig 14** Showing sections through manufactured windows with approximate dimensions

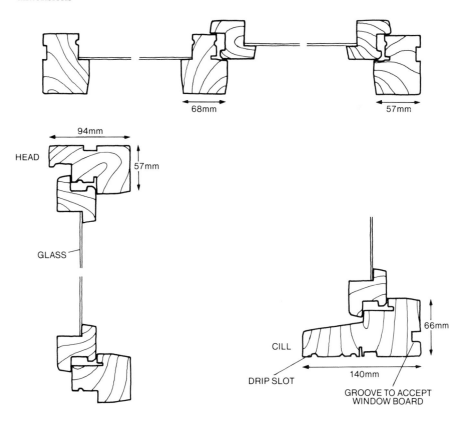

Drains in position. Manhole connected up. In the background we have bison concrete beams spanning the site to form the suspended ground floor. This provides an alternative to filling the site with approved stone covered with 100mm of concrete.

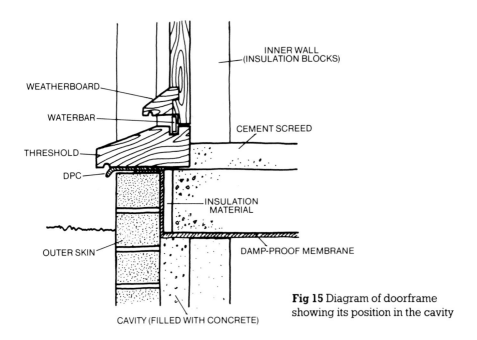

Fig 15 Diagram of doorframe showing its position in the cavity

membrane into this. Just check as you go that the cavity is empty from ground level upwards. We have filled the cavity with lean-mix concrete up to ground level but it must be clear from ground level to DPC.

We must not put it off any longer. We have to break the ice and set up a corner. A bricklayer does this on auto-pilot, without any sense of fear. The self-builder must pause for thought. There is a device on the market called a corner profile, which once set correctly perfectly controls the growth of a corner. We are using 'stretcher bond' for our brickwork and we have to ensure that a bond is maintained, both for strength and for the ultimate beauty of the masonry. We have to adhere strictly to one joint thickness throughout the building, both for the bed joints and for the perpendicular or 'perp' joints. We have to consider from the beginning the ceiling height and the window height, and we have to ensure that the windows are correctly positioned in each room. This is done by measurement along the face of the building. The vertical discipline is marked firmly on the profile stick or gauge from DPC level to window head height and thence to first floor joists, which relate to the ceiling height of the ground floor (oversite concrete plus 75mm screed plus 2.3m plus thickness of plasterboard equals position of underside of first floor joist).

The setting out of the brickwork should take into account all the openings in the walls and should absorb the discrepancies caused by the openings, so that the finished opening has perfect symmetry. This fundamental rule has vanished in the late twentieth century and the easy line is adopted. I shall show both methods and you, the self-builder striving for quality in all things, must decide.

Example one shows the perfect method were each cut in the brickwork is anticipated at DPC level and is lost under the opening, leaving the reveals in perfect harmony and bond. Example two shows the more modern approach where the window is centred to the nearest perp joint and the 'cut' or three-quarter brick is found casually forming the reveal.

With corner profile gauges there is no need to rack back the brickwork at each corner and then fill in the straight piece between: we can forge ahead, building up to window sill height without worry. The external door frames must be positioned by measurement on to the freshly bedded DPC, at the correct position over the cavity, allowing the sill to project adequately from the outside wall. The frames, indeed all frames, need support while the brickwork is surrounding them. Once they (and this applies equally to windows) are absolutely vertical you can hook a 3m (10ft) scaffold plank on to the top of the frame with a 100mm (4in) round wire nail. The nail is driven at an angle into the end of the board and hooked over the frame to allow for the whole structure to be adjusted to the spirit level; it can then be fixed by loading the plank with concrete blocks at the point where it rests on the oversite.

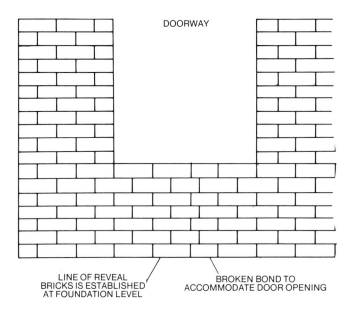

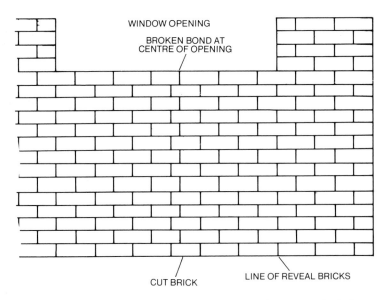

**Fig 16** Diagram showing stretcher bond with allowances for door and window openings

(*Opposite above*) Oversite concrete laid. Damp proof membrane folded back to show insulation in cavity. Drain hoppers in place. Face bricks stacked ready for use

(*Opposite below*) Stacks of facing bricks covered against rain. Internal blocks stacked on slab

## Chimneys

It is likely that a four-bedroom house will have two chimneys: one to serve a fireplace in the sitting room and the other to serve a central heating appliance. The Building Regulations pay close attention to this feature. The requirements are that sufficient non-combustible material surrounds the fire. Figure 17 shows a fireplace on an external wall with the chimney stack built externally. Note that the cavity is continued around the edifice and that the 100mm (4in) thick back to the fire must be in firebricks immediately behind the fire and thereafter must continue in class 'A' concrete blocks. Figure 17 (b) illustrates a fireplace on an external wall built internally. Notice in both cases that the jamb is not less than 200mm (8in) thick. If the fireplace is built against an internal wall then the 200mm rule also applies to the back of the fire. The fireplace in Figure 17 must have foundations and this adjustment would be made right at the beginning; the cavity must be maintained throughout. The hearth must fill the space formed by the chimney jambs and

Fig 17 Diagram to show position of fireplace on ground floor together with structural details of the base.

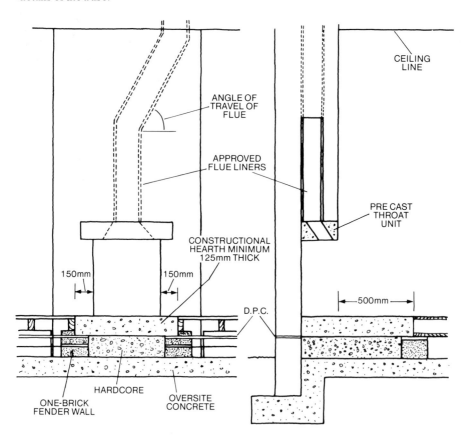

Bison beams resting on D.P.C. in between beams are laid concrete blocks to provide basis ground floor

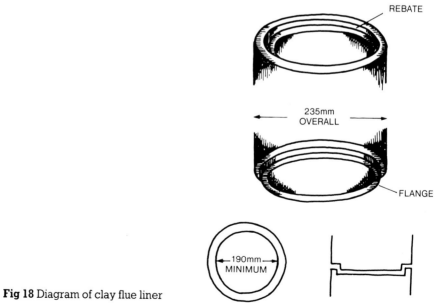

**Fig 18** Diagram of clay flue liner

must extend a minimum of 500mm (20in) forward of the jambs. It must be a minimum of 125mm (4⅞in) thick and must project not less than 150mm (6in) either side of the jamb. Above the lintel that forms the top of the fire opening it is necessary to 'gather' the chimney into a tube which will carry the smoke to the atmosphere. The core of the chimney must be formed by clay flue liners which have a rebate and socket joint. As you increase the height of the building, so you add these nice clay objects, making sure they are clean and well jointed.

So the chimney work continues at all stages throughout the building until it bursts through the roof and ends in some quiet feature, high above the garden, unnoticed and unloved, belching forth unspeakable pollution. A chimney on a gable end provides a sound buttress to the expanse of brickwork, which can suffer from wind damage at the apex. As the chimney passes through the roof a damp-proof course must be provided to ensure that rain falling on the top, exposed part of the chimney brickwork does not penetrate the roof space (see Figure 17).

### Internal Walls

You may choose to leave these until later, which means some toothing

Door frame trigged up using a scaffold plank. Vertical D.P.C. tacked in position

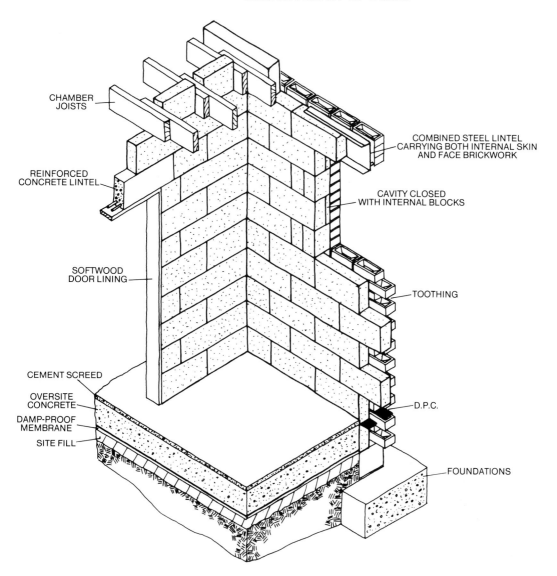

CHAMBER JOISTS

COMBINED STEEL LINTEL CARRYING BOTH INTERNAL SKIN AND FACE BRICKWORK

REINFORCED CONCRETE LINTEL

CAVITY CLOSED WITH INTERNAL BLOCKS

SOFTWOOD DOOR LINING

TOOTHING

CEMENT SCREED

OVERSITE CONCRETE

D.P.C.

DAMP-PROOF MEMBRANE

SITE FILL

FOUNDATIONS

**Fig 19** A cut-away diagram of a corner showing window reveal, internal door opening and chamber joists

must be left in the internal wall adjacent to the cross wall. The door openings in the cross walls are formed to receive a door lining at a later stage. The door lining should not be built in as you go because it will become a finished item and may become damaged or warp with exposure to dampness. The openings may be formed to a template constructed of sawn timber to the exact external dimensions of the door linings (812mm) to be used. Door linings and their properties are discussed in Chapter 6.

Let us review this phase of construction. Both the external door frames are standing, boldly, on the DPC. We have stacks of bricks and blocks conveniently spaced around the perimeter walls (and the internal walls if you decide to build them concurrently). The brickwork and blockwork can progress in smooth, even panels – remember the wall ties – up to the course of bricks on which the window frames are going to rest. You must keep the bed joint (horizontal joint) of the facing brickwork exactly level with the corresponding bed joint on the inner skin. The course of bricks which will support the windows will be marked on the profile. It is vital that the window heads all line up and therefore the sill of the window will strike a course of bricks that corresponds to its height. If, because the window height dimension does not match the brick courses, and a gap shows under the sill, this can be taken up with a row of bricks on edge or some such feature. The head of the window will normally be positioned 300mm (12in) below the ceiling on the inside. To return to the profile, the first mark made will be the ceiling height. From this you can determine the height of the head of the window.

As the work proceeds, each frame must be tied into the brickwork by means of a frame cramp. These galvanised iron straps are secured on to the side of the frame and built into the mortar joint. This must happen every three courses and great care must be exercised to keep the tail of the cramp flat so as not to 'kick' the next brick out of line. These ties must be applied to all frames and on both sides of each frame.

Each frame stands in an opening in the wall and each opening causes a bridge of the cavity construction. The cavity becomes 'closed' where the inner skin of blockwork returns to the outer skin of face brickwork to form a 'reveal'. At this junction of inner with outer skin we must apply a vertical DPC to stop the passage of rain water, absorbed into the facework, from outer to inner wall. On the horizontal brickwork we used a DPC 105mm (4¼in) wide; on the vertical junctions we must use a DPC that is 225mm (9in) wide to cover the 225mm end of the blockwork adequately at the point where it meets the frame. The simplest way to apply this membrane is to nail or tack the vertical DPC on to the window frame, allowing it to pass on to the inner face of the frame by 12mm (⅜in). This will be covered by the final plaster coat. The DPC must be fixed tightly to the frame to prevent mortar from squeezing between the frame and the membrane.

With all these thoughts and disciplines bouncing around your mind, the walls rise up on either side of the frames and the ground floor really begins to take shape. The next hurdle to overcome is the positioning of lintels over each opening. The purpose of a lintel is to support the masonry above the opening so that the force is spent within the intervening mass of masonry. Early civilisations learned how to bridge an opening with a massive stone block. This was followed by the wonderful discovery of the arch to span an opening in style and great beauty. Now we are back to lintels. For our self-build purposes there are two types of lintel to consider. The first type spans the external openings and bears both inner and outer skins of the cavity wall. These are called 'combined' lintels and are made of steel, incorporating a thin tray to pick up the brickwork and a metal box to carry the inner leaf, connected to each other by a sloping metal sheet that effectively disperses any moisture that may run down the cavity from above. The position of the lintels will be governed again by ceiling height as the first floor joists may rest on them wherever the joists coincide with an opening. The second type is the box lintel, referred to in Chapter 2, p 24.

I suggest that the brickwork and blockwork is completed all the way round the building up to the tops of window and door frames (both window and door frames will line through at their heads). Then all the lintels may be placed carefully over each opening, ensuring that the maximum bearing or overlap is achieved on to the surrounding blockwork. The ordering of lintels is mentioned in Chapter 2.

When the lintels are in place the brickwork may continue. One extra point to remember is to leave weep holes in the perp joints of the facework over each lintel to allow water to escape from the cavity. By this stage you will need temporary scaffolding on the inside and the first lift of scaffolding on the outside.

**Fig 20** Diagram of combined steel lintel (Catnic) suitable for external openings in cavity walls

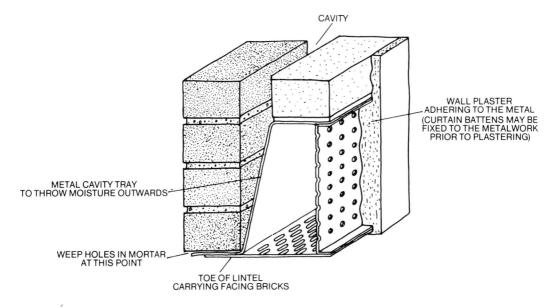

CAVITY

WALL PLASTER ADHERING TO THE METAL (CURTAIN BATTENS MAY BE FIXED TO THE METALWORK PRIOR TO PLASTERING)

METAL CAVITY TRAY TO THROW MOISTURE OUTWARDS

WEEP HOLES IN MORTAR AT THIS POINT

TOE OF LINTEL CARRYING FACING BRICKS

Cavity closed. Reveal formed against vertical D.P.C. Window frame built in

## Scaffolding

I think it is worth investing in scaffold trestles for the inside of the building, complete with perhaps thirty 3m (10ft) long scaffold planks. These light-weight trestles are fully adjustable, and answer a host of questions where 'reaching' a job is a problem. You can easily find second-hand trestles and possibly boards, but new boards are much safer and prove very satisfying. The external scaffolding is a much greater consideration. This may be a moment when you telephone a subcontractor and obtain a quotation. The price will include both hire of materials and the erection cost, or it may if you wish only cover the hire of materials, leaving you, the weary self-builder, to erect it. There are two methods of scaffolding which apply to house building: there is the 'putlog' scaffold which is actually built into the wall as you go and derives some of its support from the new wall, and there is the independent tied scaffold, which is a free-standing structure set approximately 300mm (12in) away from the building.

Putlog scaffold is economical on the use of tubing but is fixed into the wall and therefore confounds the efforts of the bricklayer, especially when pointing. Independent scaffold is free from the building and allows

**Fig 21A** Diagram of a putlog scaffold (*NB* Brace needed every fifth standard. The space between guard rail and tow board must not exceed 762mm (30in)

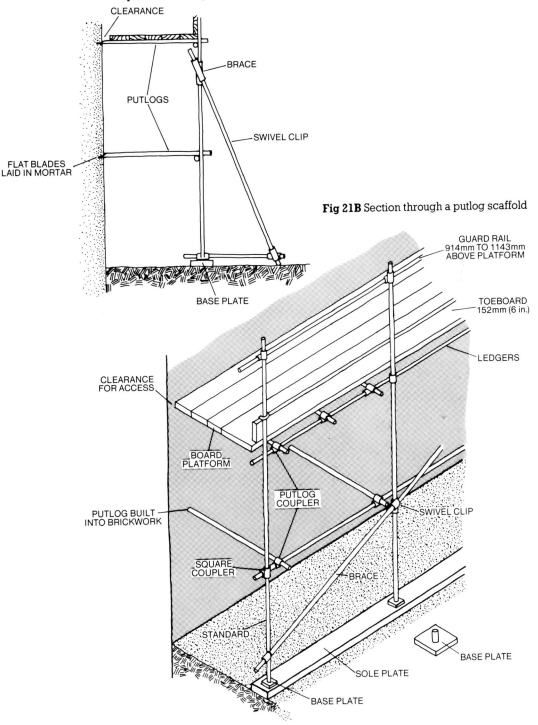

CLEARANCE

BRACE

PUTLOGS

SWIVEL CLIP

FLAT BLADES
LAID IN MORTAR

BASE PLATE

**Fig 21B** Section through a putlog scaffold

GUARD RAIL
914mm TO 1143mm
ABOVE PLATFORM

TOEBOARD
152mm (6 in.)

LEDGERS

CLEARANCE
FOR ACCESS

BOARD
PLATFORM

PUTLOG
COUPLER

SWIVEL CLIP

PUTLOG BUILT
INTO BRICKWORK

SQUARE
COUPLER

BRACE

STANDARD

BASE PLATE

SOLE PLATE

BASE PLATE

View of ceiling joists in position. Wall plate strapped to internal blockwork. Last ceiling joist close against internal skin of gable wall (150mm thick). Notice straps fixed to underside of rafters which will be built into the gable. These are called gable restraints

full access to the brickwork at all times. At Hancocks we used independent scaffold and found it to be flexible, in the sense that you could add sections with ease.

The putlog scaffold consists of a single row of standards, complete with shoes to even out the ground pressure, fixed 1.245m (4ft 1in) away from the wall, with ledger tubes fixed horizontally at 1.35m (4ft 4in) intervals to provide convenient platforms (or lifts) for the bricklayer. The putlogs are coupled to the ledgers at intervals to suit the planks used – eg a plank 38mm (1½in) thick will need support every 1.524m (5ft) – and the flattened end of the putlog is pushed into a mortar joint that has been raked out for the purpose. The scaffold is given strength by the fact that it encompasses the entire building, making it a complete square, and

(*Opposite above*) View of putlog scaffold fixed into face brickwork. This is stretcher bond

(*Opposite below*) View of first lift of scaffold showing putlogs placed on outside skin of brickwork. Butterfly wall ties in position

also by bracing it through convenient window openings. In all cases we are constructing a five-board platform complete with toe board and guard rail and safe, strong access ladder, placed and lashed to the rails at the correct angle of attack. The vertical standards need to be spaced 1.8m (5ft 10in) apart, which is suitable for loads up to 273kg per square metre.

The independent tied scaffold employs two rows of standards set apart to receive five scaffold boards and having one row of standards 300mm (12in) off the facing brickwork. It does not use putlogs but, in their place, transom tubes to bear the scaffold boards. The whole structure, and indeed all scaffolding systems, must be longitudinally braced to stop it performing a scissor movement and lowering you to the ground rather smartly.

In both methods of scaffolding there are three types of clip used. First is the putlog clip, which has an enveloping action and which clasps the

**Fig 22** Diagram of an independent scaffold

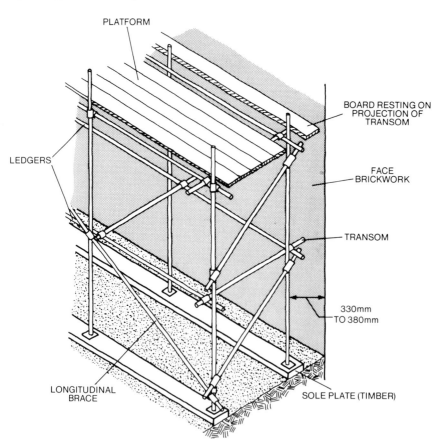

putlog in a jaw while tightening on to the ledger; this only gives strength from a downward force and must not be used anywhere but in connection with putlogs. Second there is the square coupler, which has two tightening nuts and is suitable for connecting vertical with horizontal members, ie ledgers to standards and transoms to ledgers. Third there are straight connectors, which are only suitable for connecting ledgers together. Standards are 3m or 2m in length. Ledgers are 1.8m and putlogs are 1.57m (5ft 2in). You should purchase a scaffold spanner from the builders' merchants. As you need another lift, which will occur roughly every eighteen courses of bricks (1.35m, 4ft 5in), so you add another layer of ledgers to the already upright standards and another layer of putlogs or transoms to carry the next lift of boards. Then you simply brush off the boards and raise them to the new level. Remember to remove the access ladder at night.

**Laying Bricks**
I just want to make clear the discipline of setting out brickwork and the method, thereafter, of laying each brick. The craft of bricklaying relies on rigid, determined order and the end product is marvellous to behold. As the design of many modern buildings leaves much to be desired perhaps to harp on about quality craftsmanship is like trying desperately to disguise a motorway bridge. Nevertheless, the self-builder is concerned with where everything is and how everything works and why things look the way they do. Quality brickwork begins at foundation level. On building sites thirty years ago, the labourers would sweep off the foundation concrete and then a conference would follow. The foreman would gather his bricklayers around him and armed with the plans he would lead his men around the building, marking with chalk the positions of openings and their respective reveals. Thus the bricklayers would work out all the 'cuts' (or three-quarter bricks) necessitated by the presence of the openings; working from each end of the walls, the bricklayers would lay these cut bricks at the centre point of each opening. This left the reveals in perfect brick, half-brick, brick, half-brick pattern, and the perp joints would rise out of the ground and pass on either side of the openings, continuing on up the wall to disappear into the roof. This gave the impression that the openings had 'grown' into the wall.

Once you have decided on which way to approach the setting out the problem of how to lay bricks will loom. The line will be attached to the profile gauge at each end of the wall in question. On this gauge will be marked each course and each brick joint. The line will therefore provide a guide to the perpendicular plane of the wall and to the thickness of each 'bed' joint. A trowel full of workable mortar should be rolled accurately

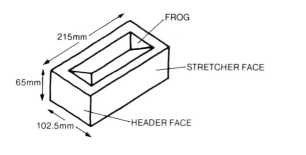

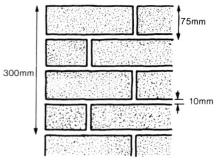

**Fig 23** Details of metric bricks shown in stretcher bond

METRIC GAUGE = 4 COURSES TO 300mm

on to the wall and smoothed, and a 'V' cut should be formed down the centre of the path of mortar. The edges should be trimmed with the trowel and the surplus mortar returned, dextrously, to the spot board. Now the next brick to be laid must have one end 'buttered' with a blob of mortar and laid on the bed of mortar, frog upwards, then tapped into place to the line, leaving a sensible perp joint between the end of the last brick and the new arrival. Any surplus mortar from the operation must be removed carefully and conveyed to the spot board. Once the row of bricks has been completed, the line may be lifted to the next mark.

The joints between the bricks are, in most places, full of mortar. At the end of a day, long before the mortar sets – and the speed of set will vary with the weather conditions – it is necessary to 'point in' all the work. A convenient and simple way to achieve a neat joint is to take a trowel full of semi-dry mortar from the edge of the spot board and, using a stick cut at an angle (the thickness of the stick being the same as the thickness of the mortar joints), push more mortar into areas deficient in mortar and smooth off all the joints. A little later, when the mortar has dried still further, you must brush the whole area with broad strokes to dislodge any crumbs of mortar left by the stick process. The whole panel of brickwork will look smooth and clear and clean. It is important that the pointing mortar is the same mix as the laying mortar so that the two processes set as one. It is vital to mix the mortar consistently throughout the building. Do not change cement brands halfway through, as the colour varies enormously. Try and calculate your total requirements for building sand and order the whole lot at once, as the loads vary in colour from one side of a pit to another. All these variations will show up in the finished brickwork. Ideally, the same person should do all the mixing throughout the building and a gauge or bucket should be used.

**First Floor Joists**
The first floor joists are timbers supporting the floor of the first floor and

forming the ceiling of the ground floor. They span from external wall (internal skin) to external wall or from convenient load-bearing partition walls to external cavity walls. The whole layout of joists for the first floor should be carefully scrutinised and physical measurements made between walls to check the lengths of timber required. It is not sufficient to scale off the plan. The spacing of the joists, which will sit on edge, must correspond to the dimensions of plasterboard sheets because they will be nailed to the underside of the joists to form the ground floor ceiling. Thus a spacing of 406mm (16in) from centre of joist to centre of joist will prove essential when nailing up sheets of plasterboard; at 406mm centres they will rest precisely halfway on each joist. If there is a partition above you must double up the joists on which it will bear. The length of span determines the depth of joist required, and wherever possible this span must be kept to a minimum to avoid using colossal baulks of timber. Broadly speaking, $1/24$ of the span + 50 equals the depth of the joist required. For example; assuming a span from wall to wall of 3.5m.

$$\frac{3500}{24} + 50 = 195.8\text{mm, say 200mm (8in)}$$

We can order the nearest stock size of timber to suit our purpose, eg 200mm × 50mm (8in × 2in) and cut the joists to length on site; again stock lengths are the norm and you, not the timber yard, must suffer the waste. It is certainly worth having the whole consignment of joists celcurized or protim treated – brush treatment is not as good. It pays to order the joists to arrive a week before you need to handle them, as they will be soaked in pickle and very unpleasant. If there are a great number to cut then hire a skill saw for the day. This will give quick, efficient cutting and the ends will be square. Get help to lift the heavy timbers into place, having first marked all their positions, with chalk, on the internal block wall. Pack up the ends with slate or bits of DPC to get the top side exactly level. If you string a taut line from the first to the last and adjust each joist between, you should achieve a perfect level. Any variations in the thickness (depth) of the joist will throw up a problem on the ground floor ceiling, but this will be lost in the plaster work. If the variation is enormous then throw the timber back at the merchant.

The Building Regulations state that all timber to be used structurally in a building should be stress graded (see Building Regulations approved document, 1985, 'Structures'). That means that every piece of timber must be visually inspected and all imperfect lengths pulled out. Ninety per cent of all timber is now stress graded to an approved standard. The timber, having been graded, will bear a stamp in red ink – probably GS, standing for general stress grading. Always ask for stress graded, treated timber. The Building Regulations document mentioned above is very useful for sizing timbers for all building purposes.

When the first floor joists encounter a chimney breast they must be 'trimmed' around the obstruction and suspended from a trimmer joist, which in turn is connected to the nearest whole joist on either side of the obstruction. The trimmer joist may be traditionally fixed to the adjacent joists by a tusk tenon, which is fearfully difficult to execute, or, more within the range of the self-builder, by means of a joist hanger. Perhaps you might find a local carpenter who remembers how to form a tusk tenon.

As illustrated in Figure 00, the joist hanger is a galvanised metal ledge that is designed to receive a 50mm (2in) or 75mm (3in) piece of timber, while being easily nailed to the relevant joist from which it gains its support.

**Fig 24** Diagram to show chamber joists in relation to first floor fireplace with trimming joist in position. The same construction method would apply to an internal chimney breast on the first floor without a fireplace

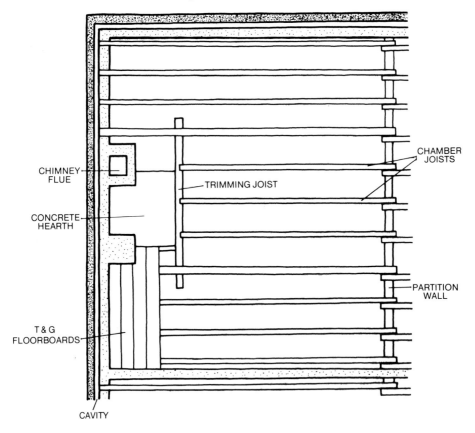

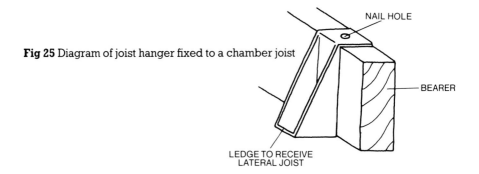

**Fig 25** Diagram of joist hanger fixed to a chamber joist

A trimming detail is necessary around the stair well. If a joist runs parallel to a wall then it should be set off from the finished face of the wall by 38mm (1½in). No joist must pass within 38mm of the surface of a chimney breast.

When the joists are raised and level, nail a length or several lengths of 38mm × 19mm (1½in × ¾in) tile batten to the top surface of the joists to hold them steady while the blocks are laid between the timbers. As soon as the blockwork is filled in and the joists are secure, the cavity wall may progress upwards, using the new-found security of the first floor joists as a platform bridged by trusty scaffold planks, four or five wide.

Let us review the scaffold position at this point. We can use our first floor skeleton, inside, to provide a platform while, outside, we should have a lift of scaffold finishing 2.7m (8ft 9in) from the ground. As our ceiling height is 2.3m (7ft 6in) the inner and outer scaffold platforms are similar in height. Of course, you may choose to use trestles to reach the first lift, ie to the top of the ground floor window, and construct the first lift of scaffolding at the 2.7m level.

The placing of first floor joists presupposes that the partition walls and chimneys are up to ceiling height.

These long lengths of timber spanning rooms are liable to twist. To prevent this we must introduce a central line of support known as 'herringbone strutting'. This may be done in 40mm × 40mm (1½in × 1½in) timber or by using a purpose-made metal strut.

**Fig 26** Diagram of herringbone strutting

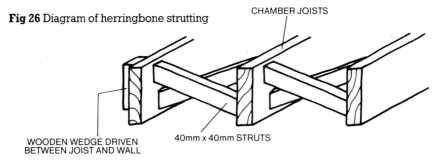

83

If you use wood, here is a guide. Assuming we have 200mm × 50mm (8in × 2in) joists mark a pencil line down the centre of the span of joists. At each end where the last joist meets the wall, drive wooden wedges between joist and wall. Now mark two further lines parallel to the centre line and 90mm (3½in) out from it, thus producing two lines 180mm (7in) apart. Lay your 40mm × 40mm (1½in × 1½in) batten diagonally across two joists at the points where the outside lines intersect. In the angle formed by the joist, the pencil line and the batten, you can mark the batten so that, when cut, it will fit perfectly between the two joists concerned. Fix the two cut battens from the top of one joist to the bottom of the other along the centre line described above. The difference between herringbone strutting and solid bridging is that no matter what shrinkage or movement occurs in the joists, the effect will be to tighten the strutting. The battens are cut at 180mm (7in), not 200mm (8in), to allow for any movement and to stop them ever fouling the ceiling or the floor to which they are adjacent.

### First Floor Joists to Wall-Plate

Now we repeat the lessons learned on the ground floor and slowly but surely reach the wall-plate, on which will rest the roof. The ceiling height in the bedrooms on the first floor is, let us say, 2.3m (7ft 6in) and the position of the heads of the windows will line through immediately beneath the wall-plate. Mark the courses of bricks on the profile gauge and raise the brickwork and blockwork up to the course immediately beneath the windows. Position windows with raking planks on to the new first floor joists and build in around them, using frame cramps, vertical DPC and all the skill thus far developed. The inner walls may be continued, making provision for door openings. Stack the blocks on the scaffold inside, taking care not to overload the new floor joists. The facing bricks need to be carried up the access ladder on to the external scaffold, either six at a time or, if you have one, in a hideous medieval instrument called a 'hod'. Cement mortar, mixed at a consistent ratio of sand to cement, remember, can be lifted in buckets on a pulley wheel fixed to a scaffold standard halfway along the building. Another access ladder must be secured in the stair well to give access to the first floor.

When the brickwork is level with the heads of the windows, the external wall is complete save for the gables and the chimneys. Let us assume that the facework finishes at the tops of the windows; therefore the internal wall which will bear the roof will continue one course above the first floor windows. The difference in height between the inner and outer walls is governed by the angle of pitch of the roof. The angle at which the rafter passes over the outer wall must be sufficient to provide adequate soffit. More discussion on this point will be held in Chapter 5.

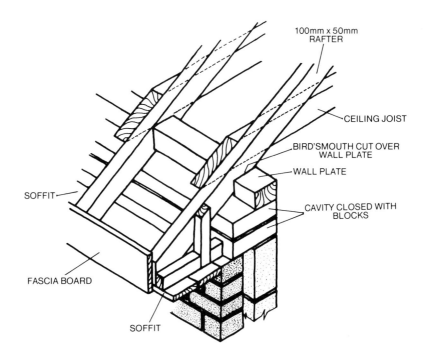

**Fig 27** Diagram showing detail of eaves. Note especially the way in which the cavity is closed

The best way for the self-builder to avoid catastrophe at the eaves is to build in a combined Catnic-type lintel over the head of the window so that, should the height of the external wall have to be adjusted to meet the rafters, there is a bearing on which to build. So generally, the facing brickwork finishes at the top of the window while the internal blockwork continues for one more course (225mm, 9in) before accepting the wall-plate. Where there is an opening, this is bridged with a 225mm box lintel or, as mentioned previously, and for very little extra cost, a combined lintel. The last job before bedding on the wall-plate is to close off the cavity. This is a fire regulation and its purpose is to exclude fire from the cavity, thus arresting its spread to the roof. To achieve this we need a brick laid sideways up against the outer face of the inner skin. This leaves a 50mm (2in) edge on which to rest the soffit.

One last surge of effort is required to prepare the whole building to receive its well-earned roof. We are now 'plate high', which is a significant festival in the construction industry. Make a dash for the woodpile and select enough straight 100mm × 75mm (4in × 3in) timber to circumnavigate the internal walls on which the roof will rest. Where there needs to be a join, cut a half-joint. Lay a bed of mortar and tap the timber plate into position, making sure it is firmly resting on the wall throughout its length. When the mortar is dry you can drive 100mm (4in) cut nails through the plate and into the top course of blocks. You also need to fix galvanised iron straps to the wall-plate at 1200mm centres which will be nailed to the face of the inner skin, thus restraining the wall-plate.

On the night you reach plate high you have good cause to celebrate. The heavy building, apart from the roof tiles, is behind you. The massive task of lifting tons of materials up into the air and bringing them to rest in some order is finished. Only the gables remain, and these cannot be attempted until the physical shape of the roof is known.

# 5
# THE ROOF

The view from the site hut is of a hollow box five metres high surrounded in tubular scaffolding. The phase that follows is unquestionably the most dramatic visually. At the end of the roof phase you no longer need the scaffolding. It may be 'struck' and carried away. The moment is like the launching of a new ship.

## The Pitched Roof

We shall consider a pitched roof to suit a gable-ended building, as in describing this structure we meet all the forces that must be reckoned with and tamed. The pitched roof most effectively spans a building; it becomes stronger as the pitch or steepness increases; it sheds the rain most quickly and enhances the building with lovely proportion. The steepness or flatness of the pitched roof will be determined at the planning stage, and your plan can be scaled off with a scale rule to find the exact rafter length. Should you wish to check this dimension further you can do so in the peace and tranquillity of the site hut. Draw on graph paper a large triangle, the baseline of which measures the same as the distance between the internal walls of the house, wall-plate to wall-plate. Now, using a protractor mark an angle to the horizontal of, say, 40° (concrete interlocking tiles, for example, will work on roofs having a pitch of between 35° and 45°) at both ends of your baseline. Extend these

**Fig 28** To show a section through a traditional roof

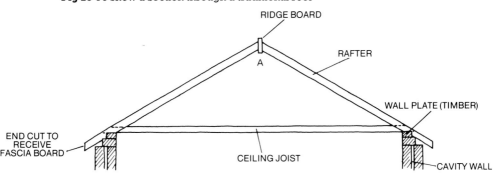

87

lines until they meet at the ridge or apex of the triangle. Now you can accurately scale off the lengths of the rafters, but remember to allow an overhang of 600mm (2ft), which will be cut off later to accept the fascia-board.

The angle of the pitch is that which it makes with the horizontal. Thus the angle that is formed where the rafter meets the ridge-board at the apex will be $90° - 40° = 50°$. This we shall need in a moment.

## Ceiling Joists

The first actual task is to select the correct number of ceiling joists. These will often be 100mm × 50mm (4in × 2in) in dimension, but with the future development of the roof space in mind it may be wise to use more substantial timbers, dependent on the span involved. The ceiling joists must be laid on the wall-plate at 406mm centres, just as with the first floor joists, to receive plasterboard forming the first floor ceiling. Check the measurement between wall-plates. Working off the outside scaffold at a height 450mm (18in) below the wall-plate to provide comfortable working conditions, but no higher (otherwise the platform will foul the future construction of fascia-board and rainwater gutter), begin to mark the position of the centre of each joist on the wall-plate. Now, at ground level on a trestle work-bench, mark and cut the ceiling joists to length with the skill saw. Carry them aloft. Project them across the building, taking care not to rub and therefore damage the wall-plate. Nail each one in position by means of a 100mm (4in) round wire nail on the 'skew'.

The ceiling joist has two functions: it holds up the first floor ceiling and it resists the tendency that the top of the building may have to spread under the weight of the tiled roof. The 'skew' nail, therefore, is grossly inadequate for such a trojan task and you score a red star for quality if you drill, later, the rafter and ceiling joist and bolt the union together using timber connectors. This helps to hold the triangle together and leaves the skew nail to concentrate on fixing the joist to the wall-plate.

For the next operation we can use the new joists as a platform. I think it is wise first to give additional support from underneath the joists. Nail a plank to the underside of the new ceiling joists. Cut two or three lengths of 100mm × 50mm timber just 12mm (½in) longer than the vertical distance between the chamber joists and the first floor ceiling joists. It should be 2.3m plus 19mm (¾in) allowing for the board flooring plus 10mm (⅜in) allowing for the plasterboard ceiling to the first floor, ie 2.329m. These upright timbers must be skew nailed to a scaffold plank running down the centre of the chamber joists (across them naturally). The net effect will be to brace the ceiling joists to enable you to lay a five- or six-board platform down the centre of the building.

From this you will easily, off a trestle or similar hop-up, reach the ridge-board when it is in position.

This is the moment to raise your new roof tank into the newly conquered roof space and put it to one side.

## Rafters

The timber that forms the sloping side of our pitched roof is called the rafter. Rafters travel in pairs, and their dimensions are invariably 100mm × 50mm (4in × 2in). There will be the same number of rafters as there are ceiling joists. We have decided on the length of rafter, allowing enough of an overhang at the exterior walls to enable us to terminate the rafter in an orderly fashion. Take two rafters and lay them on the bench. Cut one end at 50° using a carpenter's adjustable square, for this cut face will meet the ridge-board and form the apex (eg 90° − 40° which is the pitch = 50°). Now measure from the inside of the cut (see Figure 28 at point A on the diagram down the rafter to determine the junction with the wall-plate. This junction is termed the 'bird's-mouth'. There are various rules governing the bird's-mouth. It is vital to cut your bird's-mouth neatly so that the joint with the wall-plate meets on all sides. No less important is the ridge cut at the opposite end of the rafter which must meet the ridge exactly to provide strength at the apex. Truss rafters probably score heavily at this point when their ridge joints (they do not have ridge-boards) are made on a factory bench and are then gang nailed together. Do not forget to allow 12mm (½in) in your calculation

**Fig 29** Diagram illustrating the bird's mouth cut at the junction of rafter and wall plate

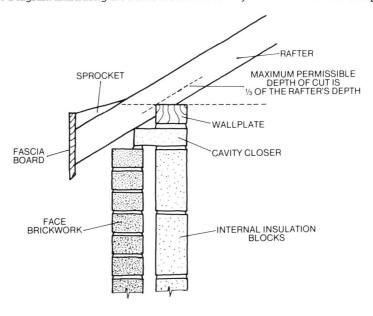

to represent half the ridge-board, otherwise your ridge cuts will not meet exactly.

I suggest that you set out the angle of pitch on a piece of plywood and transfer this to the rafter by laying the rafter across the plywood and marking the horizontal or 'seat' cut by physically lining up the rafter. From this you can mark the vertical cut, which must not penetrate the rafter by more than one-third of the rafter's width. The vertical cut on the bird's-mouth will be exactly parallel to the ridge cut. You can use your plywood triangle denoting the pitch of roof (representing half the roof only) to mark the horizontal line, and thereafter the vertical cut. The ridge-board must stand above the rafter by the thickness of the top tile batten. The initial 'rearing' of the roof is tricky. More than ever before you need a friend. You have got to raise the two pairs of rafters simultaneously at either end of the building, complete with ridge-board.

Fear not. If you have no friends you need to build a short tower scaffold at the gable ends of the building to act as a temporary support while you struggle with the first bones of the roof. This tower is easily hired from a hire shop and it comes in 600mm (2ft) sections. You will need four sections at each end.

Lay the two pairs of rafters on the temporary platform upon the ceiling joists. Nail a 50mm × 50mm (2in × 2in) batten across both members of each pair at a point just below the 50° splay cut. This batten will act as a cradle and turns your rafters into nutcrackers. Raise one nutcracker one end, and the other the other end. Position the pairs of rafters with their feet on the corresponding marks made on the surface of the wall-plate. Adjust the two pairs until they are vertical. Now measure and cut the 170mm × 40mm (7in × 1½in) board in such a way that it provides a continuous ridge on which all the rafters may rest. There are two methods of joining a ridge-board. The ridge must present an absolutely flat surface to the rafter ends. There must be no warping or twisting or strange goings on. Either you cut an incredibly complicated joint like a Chinese puzzle with folding wedges at its centre that have the job of forcing the two shoulders of the joint into a lavish embrace, or you cut a giant 'dovetail'. Both methods earn you red stars for effort and prove beyond question that you are a self-builder seeking quality and excellence in all things. Raise up the ridge-board and rest it in the cradle provided so that it spans from pattern rafter to pattern rafter. If this looks right and the rafter cuts all meet their respective surfaces firmly and squarely, then the rest of the rafters may be cut using the pattern rafter to mark the others.

When all the pairs of rafters are cut and the fresh sawn cuts have been bathed in preservative it remains to nail each rafter, starting from the middle and working to either end, at the ridge-board and into the wall-

**Fig 30** Diagram of rafters meeting the ridgeboard

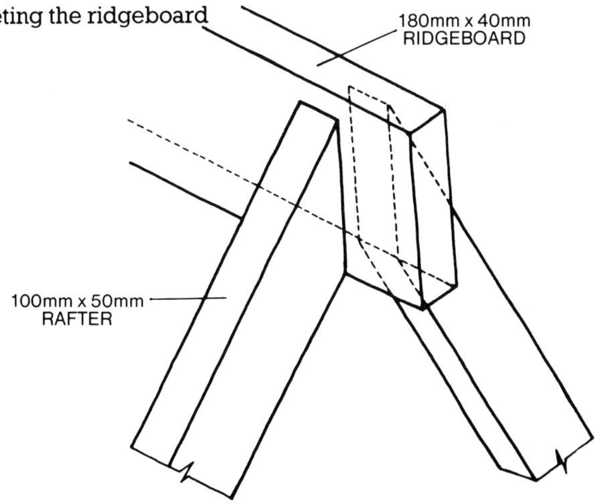

180mm x 40mm
RIDGEBOARD

100mm x 50mm
RAFTER

plate. Do the rafters in pairs – do not continue down one side and then fix the other side. The ridge must be watched for straightness at all times. Each rafter must be nailed or bolted to the neighbouring ceiling joist.

The common rafters need further support and this is provided by the purlin. The purlin is a stout timber whose dimensions may vary from 150mm × 50mm (6in × 2in) to 225mm × 50mm (9in × 2in), depending on the length of the rafters and the distance between load-bearing walls off which the purlin can be braced. Thus the purlin is nailed midway between wall-plate and ridge to the underside of each rafter. The ends of the purlins are built into the inner skin on the cavity wall. If you need to join two timbers to form a purlin, the joint should be over a strutting point. When the purlin passes over a load-bearing wall that terminates in the roof space, a short 150mm × 50mm prop should be cut and wedged between the top of the wall and the purlin, giving additional support to the roof to withstand the loading of the roof tiles. Allow the purlins to run over the cavity wall at each gable. The exact length can be assessed when the blockwork is continued.

Two final tasks before retiring to the site hut. Cut and trim a trapdoor opening for access to the roof space. Cut and lay three rows of 100mm × 50mm (4in × 2in) timber across the top of the ceiling joists, spiking each joist, to give additional support. If the ceiling joists are deep enough (eg 150mm × 50mm) you could use herringbone strutting as for the chamber joists; this has the added advantage of keeping below the floor line should you decide to develop and use the attic.

*Trussed Rafters*
All our discussions regarding the roof have so far dealt with the 'traditional roof', recycling age-old methods of spanning space. As the cost of

Roof trusses in position. Soffit board wedged down onto the top of the face brickwork

timber has risen and risen and the cost of labour has closely followed, the trussed rafter has evolved. By employing accurate geometry the trussed rafter can be constructed out of more slender timber. It is, therefore, lighter and cheaper than its traditional equivalent. A host of companies now offer a complete design and fabrication service. You send them dimensions on an order form and the rafters will be purpose-made and delivered to your site. They are lifted into position and spiked on to the wall-plate, as per manufacturer's instructions, greatly speeding up the roofing process. They are perfectly sound and solid and cheap, but to a self-builder they may lack quality. They reduce that sense of originality; they fill your roof space with a forest of timber, none of which may be cut. This is one of the areas where the self-builder may make his mark; it satisfies medieval traditions of primitive shelters and sound, wooden roofs. How often does the manufactured article faintly approach the quality of the handmade?

## Gables
The roof carcass is a very impressive sight and should be admired from a distance, and photographed even, with the head of its creator poking

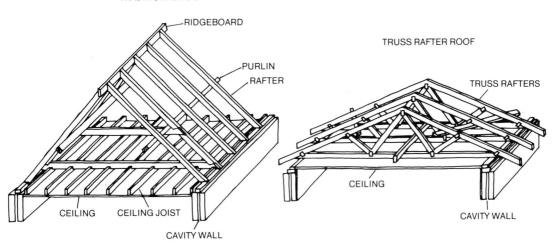

**Fig 31A** Drawing to show a traditional roof alongside a truss rafter roof

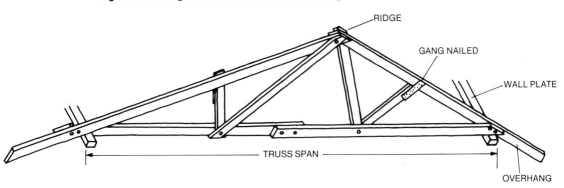

**Fig 31B** Diagram of a truss rafter

through the straight lines of the rafters. We now have a very definite shape to which we can add both gables. If the chimneys are on the gables then the whole mass of masonry comes up together. The problem of weathering or waterproofing the chimney has a solution calling for immense skill and patience. The theory is to make sure any rain falling on or around the chimneys is quickly deflected on to the surface of the tiles or slates and thence to the gutter. The process is called 'flashing' and uses lead, and lead is the province of plumbers (*plumbum* is Latin for lead). The principle is basically this: into brickwork is inserted a length of lead cut into steps, each step corresponding to a bed joint in the brick-work. The steps are cut to follow the pitch of the roof and the tail of the lead sheet is skilfully dressed out over the finished tilework. Underneath each tile that abuts the chimney is inserted a lead soaker with an upstand of 75mm (3in) and a flat surface of 100mm (4in). The flat part of the

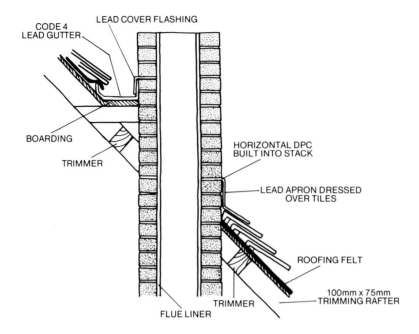

CODE 4
LEAD GUTTER

LEAD COVER FLASHING

BOARDING

TRIMMER

HORIZONTAL DPC
BUILT INTO STACK

LEAD APRON DRESSED
OVER TILES

ROOFING FELT

100mm x 75mm
TRIMMING RAFTER

TRIMMER

FLUE LINER

**Fig 32** Section through chimney stack

soaker sits under the tile while the upstand rests against the chimney. Thus any water that attempts to run under the lead step flashing will encounter the soaker and will be caused to run out on the surface of the tile immediately beneath it. Any water hitting the chimney will simply run over the step flashing and on to the tiles. The idea of lead flashing applies everywhere a roof is penetrated by or abutted to an obstacle such as a chimeny. Flashing has got to work – poor leadwork brings endless misery. Perhaps this is a time when the self-builder should give in and reach for the telephone.

Meanwhile the gable brickwork and blockwork continues; all the rules of good workmanship are observed, with clean cavities, carefully positioned wall-ties and bricks and blocks precisely cut to keep within the line prescribed by the last pair of rafters. The cutting of the bricks and blocks can easily be accomplished using a lump hammer and bolster. It is very important to keep the cavity wall inner and outer skins below the line of the last rafter, because the tile battens will fly over the gable wall and terminate over the cavity. You must provide lateral restraint to the gable by means of metal straps laid along the rafters and built into the inner skin.

**Preparing the Roof for Tiling**
With the gables up and the chimneys through the roof but not neces-

sarily finished, the race is on to get the building 'dry'. Let us assume we wish to use plain tiles as our roof covering. This system will make the self-builder conversant with the principles of roofing, which vary slightly when using large interlocking tiles or slates.

Plain tiles vary in colour according to the clay from which they are made and vary in size according to whether they are machine- or hand-made. They measure 265mm (10½in) by 165mm (6½in). They are laid on the roof in courses, each course being fixed or hung on battens, which in turn are soundly nailed to each rafter. The job of battening the roof is a most satisfying one and I strongly recommend you tackle this. The bundles of 38mm × 19mm (1½in × ¾in) sawn timber, completely soaked in preservative, will have been delivered with the roof timbers and should be protected from cloudbursts. Tile battens are cut in random lengths and bundled up to give an overall total of 'running' metres; this is a term often used in building when describing overdrafts and continuous unspecified lengths of timber. To calculate that 'running' figure you have to know the gauge at which the tiles, and hence the battens, are to be laid. If the gauge is 100mm (4in) you divide the

**Fig 33** Details of plain roofing tiles

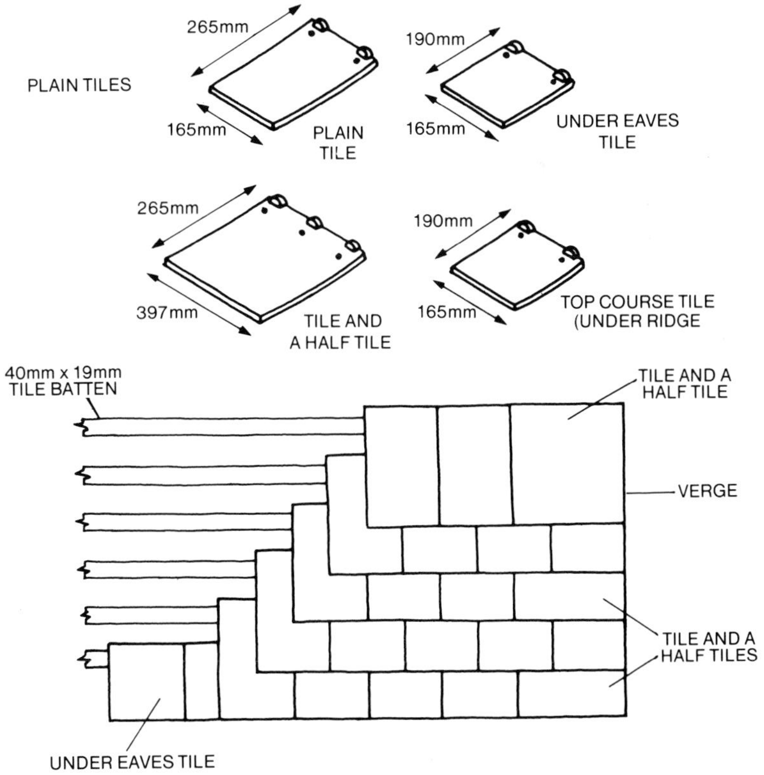

length of rafter by 100mm and multiply by two (both sides of the roof). This gives the actual number of battens required and this figure must be multiplied by the length of the roof (gable to gable) to discover the total number of running metres required. Carry your bundles on to the scaffold. Cut the strings.

The ends of the rafters have been left, oversailing the walls for future modification. The moment is upon us. The ends of the rafters support, and are covered by, the fascia-board. The purpose of the fascia is to provide a clean, decorated line at the bottom of the roof, a sort of margin between roof and wall, and to provide a fixing for the rainwater gutter. It consists of prepared (ie planed up) timber boards measuring 200mm × 25mm (8in × 1in) with a groove at the bottom edge to accept the soffit-board. String a building line from one end of the building to the other, attached to the end rafters at a height pre-ordained by considerations such as whether the first floor windows will open or not and how the eaves projection will look in relation to the roof itself. In the case of our example, the soffit-board will rest above the top of the windows (and along the entire wall at that level) so to obtain your mark at either end you must, using a spirit level placed on the wall, draw a line across the rafter, giving you the position of the intended soffit-board. It is interesting to note that the word 'soffit' may be used in connection with any building component which has an 'underside', eg a stairway, lintel or

**Fig 34** Section through eaves showing position of fascia and soffit

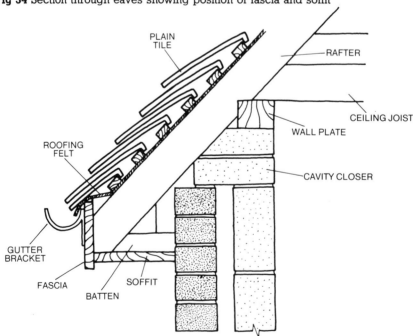

PLAIN TILE

RAFTER

CEILING JOIST

WALL PLATE

ROOFING FELT

CAVITY CLOSER

GUTTER BRACKET

FASCIA

SOFFIT

BATTEN

Close up of fascia, soffit and wallplate          Roof carcass with fascia in position

arch. It is derived from the Latin *suffixus* – something underneath. Now make a vertical line on the end rafter to correspond with the position of the fascia, allowing for the exact position of the soffit groove already inscribed on the fascia-board. Where the vertical mark surfaces on the top side of the rafter, drive in a small nail and fix the line. Repeat the process at the other end. Saw off each rafter to the mark and treat the fresh cut ends. Offer up the ready primed fascia-board and soundly nail to each joist using two-inch nails. The fascia must protrude above the joist to allow the eaves to lie neatly, and should provide a slight upturn to the tiles. The first tile to be laid will be the eaves tiles, which will protrude over the fascia, followed by the first plain tiles, which will finish at the same level as the eaves or under-eaves tiles. The first batten to fix therefore must be the one to take the eaves tiles. Go back to the site hut and bring out the sarking or underfelt. This will provide a basic layer of waterproofing should a tile break in the future. Roll out the one-metre-wide sheet and position it so that the leading edge is turned down into the gutter (not yet fixed). Nail a batten, without driving home the nails, at the top edge of the sheet but 150mm (6in) down from the actual edge to allow for a 150mm overlap when applying the next sheet. Continue this up to the ridge on both sides. Now fix the eave batten, using an eave tile to correctly gauge the overhang of the fascia. The next batten will carry the first true plain tile. The gauge or distance from centre of batten to centre of batten will vary with different tiles, but for plain tiles, which must have a 'lap' not less than 63mm (2½in) depending on the manufacturer's instructions, you will need a gauge of 101mm (4in). The formula to calculate gauge is length of tile (265mm) minus the lap (63mm) divided by two; in this example $(265 - 63)/2 =$ a gauge of 101mm. I suggest you cut three blocks of wood of 101mm thickness and use these as spacers when setting out each batten. So from the first batten, having nailed this at every rafter with a 38mm (1½in) galvanised round-headed nail, you place three blocks along the length of the roof and nudge the next batten against the blocks, giving you the 101mm spacing. Any batten that needs to be cut must be cut back with a bow saw to the nearest rafter centre, giving you enough room to start the next length of batten on the same rafter, allowing a 25mm (1in) bearing for each batten end. Continue like this on both sides until you reach the ridge. Do not put your boot through the felt; you are creating a 'ladder' of battens as you go, so there is no excuse.

You have reached another solstice in your project – the building is now dry. The trade call the condition 'felt and battened'. From this day forth you are protected from the weather, and inside building work can progress whatever the season, day or night. Storage of materials is made simple. The site hut may begin to lose its charm; however, I would resist the temptation to transfer your headquarters into the house as you will constantly be moving them from room to room ahead of the work.

## Tiling the Roof

There is perhaps a more urgent watershed to move towards rapidly and that involves the total removal of the scaffold. As this is a hired item every week counts. First, we must tile the roof and give it the lasting cover to withstand the elements for a hundred years. We have decided on plain tiles as they illustrate most of the main principles of tiling. Marley Tile Company and Redland Tile Company offer a tiling system that exchanges the tile unit for a much larger concrete object in a variety of colours. They are popular, quick to assemble and can be used on roof pitches as low as 17°, whereas plain tiles are not effective on pitches of less than 40°. So to the plain tiles, which form a far prettier roof.

The plain tiles are most likely to arrive on an enormous waggon direct from the manufacturer. They will be stacked on pallets and covered in a plastic sheet. Once again, you may be able to borrow a fork-lift machine mounted on the back of a tractor for the day on which the tiles are due to arrive. Whatever happens you must have some sort of machine to assist in the off-loading. This was an awful moment at Hancocks. I well remember it: the tiles arrived on a monster among articulated lorries; the driver had come straight from the Midlands and was fed up. It was out of the question that he should even attempt to negotiate the site. There he stood, or rather steamed, the rain causing his three windscreen wipers to beat like the wings of a heron. The width of our road at this point is perhaps ten feet at the most. The vehicle was eight feet wide, leaving two feet for the school bus, the fire engine and the ambulance. You suddenly feel hopelessly alone; you wish you could move away. The valley is blocked. We had borrowed an old digger machine (excavator) built around a Fordson tractor with a 'Bermuda' cab, which meant that it let everything in – sun in Bermuda, no doubt, but rain and sleet in Britain. My friend and I pushed spare putlogs under the pallets. The driver gave us some webbing slings and we attached these to the front bucket of the excavator, now jammed between the ditch and the side of the silent artic. We roared the engine of the tractor to its maximum effort and summoned all the horsepower it could muster. Above the din there was a creaking sound the the first of five pallets left the bed of the lorry. Through a mist of hydraulic oil atomising from every hose the pallet descended with majesty to the side of the ditch. With furious manoeuvring on behalf of the tractor driver, we safely lowered four pallets to terra firma. The last pallet caught the side of the lorry and spilled with a desperate crash into the ditch. One-fifth of the Hancocks lovely new roof, straight from the manufacturer, into the ditch.

This could have been avoided in one of two ways. First, hire a fork-lift machine from a farmer; park the articulated lorry in a layby or farmyard; ferry the pallets slowly and comfortably on to the site, placing them as near to the scaffold as possible. Alternatively, have the manufacturer deliver to your local merchant and instruct him to deliver the tiles in small quantities which you can off-load by hand.

Let us hope that our tiles are near the scaffold access ladder (you can move the ladder to reach the tiles) and that the correct colour and number of tiles have been delivered, complete with suitable 'fittings'. Tile fittings are all the necessary side issues that complete your roof, such as under-eave tiles, 'tile and a halfs', and the ridge tiles. The quantities of all these items is discussed in Chapter 2.

Sweep the scaffold clean of any debris from the previous operation, for this next task is a steady trudge. You have to carry the plain tiles on your shoulder, ten at a time, up the ladder, along the scaffold, via a purpose-made hop-up, on to the roof and up the tile battens to the relevant position, where you must transfer them deftly from your shoulder (possibly reinforced with some foam padding) to a special little stack propped on the roof battens. The professional tiler will smoke in the site hut until his agile labourer has 'loaded' the roof. The self-builder, on the other hand, must steel himself to the task and rest easy in the knowledge that his cardiovascular fitness will be hugely increased. It is important to load the roof from both sides at once to even out the stress on the timber carcass. As it is difficult to judge the spacing of the little tile stacks, you may feel happier loading a section either side and then laying those tiles before continuing with the loading.

The first course of tiles is laid at fascia board level with sufficient over-hang to drop the rain water into the centre of the gutter. We start off the tiling with a course of under-eave tiles (see Figure 34). Lay a complete course of under-eave tiles right along the roof, hanging on the first batten and not nailed. This exercise will throw up the snags. The chances of your roof length exactly accommodating a whole number of plain tiles are remote. It may have been designed to take an exact number of tiles at 165mm (6½in) in width. A variation of 25mm (1in) over the length will mean that you have to cut a tile to fit. Tile widths themselves may vary a fraction of a millimetre, which when multiplied by the number of tiles in one course will throw up a variation. The snag or 'cut' arising from all this must be lost in the centre of the roof, where it will pass unnoticed. If you have to cut one tile in every course on both sides of the roof you might wish to leave all the cuts until last. Also do not forget you must leave access on to the roof. I suggest a 600mm (2ft) avenue be left untiled from the eaves to the ridge, in the centre of the building, which will incorporate the cut tiles at the end as you tile yourself off the roof. Pro-

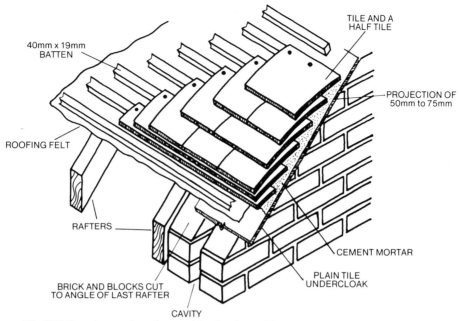

**Fig 35A** Drawing to show bonnet hip tiles in position

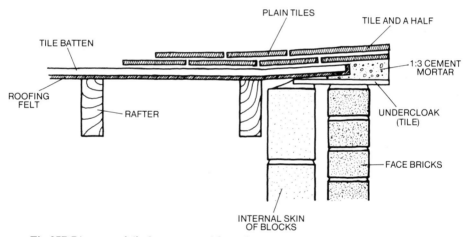

**Fig 35B** Diagram of tiled verge at gable end

viding the gables are parallel, the size of cut tile will not vary from course to course.

Begin laying plain tiles from the eaves upwards, beginning each course at either gable. Each course will start with a plain tile and the course above that will start with a tile and a half to create a 'bond' (side lap). The detail of roof meeting cavity wall at the gable is tricky and involves cement work. We have to close the cavity, project the roof tiles over the gable wall both to protect the top of the wall and to jettison any rainwater

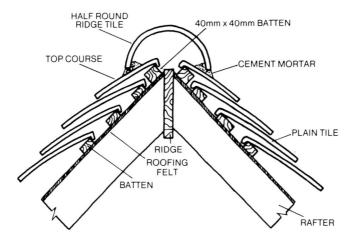

**Fig 36** Section through ridge of traditional roof

drips clear of the gable wall, and we have to make sure the cement pointing is strong and neat. This area of the building is most inaccessible for future repair work.

The tile battens have been set to fly over the cavity. A plain tile is pushed under the battens and over to reach the inner skin of blockwork, and is allowed to project over the outer skin by 75mm (3in). Nail a 75mm rough batten to the gable brickwork with 100mm (4in) cut nails (or masonry nails) to provide a guide and a support for the plain tile or 'undercloak', as it is described. You have two choices in how to approach the cement work: either you keep a bucket of 4 : 1 mortar on the scaffold at each gable end or you leave the cement work until the end. The argument for doing it at the end is that you have finished all hammering and moving on the roof which might disturb your cementing. I think if you are careful not to charge about like a Minotaur, you should proceed with the finishing of the verge as you go, apart from perhaps the final pointing, which can be done off the gable lift of scaffold.

The end tiles (either plain tiles or tile and a halfs) must be bedded on mortar which is located on the plain tile undercloak. The last tiles should sweep upwards very slightly, to cause rain water to run back on to the roof rather than over the gable. Continue to lay the plain tiles, pushing them firmly together and nailing every fourth course with one galvanised nail to each tile. Remember to load the roof evenly.

When you reach the ridge at either end, again the ridge tile must be bedded on to the top course of tiles with cement mortar. If possible you should bed on the ridge tiles at either end and then run a building line between the two to ensure that the ridge is absolutely straight and level. It is very noticeable from ground level if the ridge rises and falls like a switchback. The ridge tiles should be pointed as you go and any surplus mortar wiped off.

Over the bathroom we must make provision in the roof to vent the drainage system. The pipework is called the 'soil vent' and is dealt with in Chapter 6 (p 122). A 150mm (6in) plastic pipe must pass through the roof tiles, and where it passes through the tiling we must concentrate on weathering the junction. You should obtain a long length of the plastic pipe and stand it in position according to the plan, so that it finishes at the correct height above the eaves, passing through a hole in the felt and thus into the air. Pass over the top of the pipe a weather slate and pull this down to tile level. Tile around the metal collar as per manufacturer's instructions, which do vary from one to another. Common sense will indicate what we hope to achieve.

Plain tiles are extremely difficult to cut with accuracy. The only method I have succeeded with is the use of pinchers, which when new and sharp will bite off chunks of the tile back to a line scored on the surface at the required position. Wear a glove when attempting the cuts. Another method is to hire a petrol-driven brick- or stone-cutting disc saw, which although noisy, dusty and costly will execute your cuts very quickly.

Take care to point in the verges from the scaffold platform. Brush off the work with a soft brush, sweep the scaffold and collect the broken tiles into a bucket. If you flick them off the scaffold carelessly, you will only have to pick them out of the mud later on.

## Guttering

The next job is to fix the rainwater gutter to the fascia. The object is to convey storm water quickly from the roof to the nearest downpipe, which is located over the gullies leading to the soakaways. Assuming that on a gable-ended house we have four downpipes, one at each corner, then the fall of the gutter, which determines the flow of the water, must be from the centre of the building down to each end. This means that the gutter has to travel across the fascia, losing height from the centre to the ends. Fix a nail into the centre of the fascia 50mm (2in) from the top of the board. Run a line out to both gable ends and fix nails such as to give a slight fall. Too savage a fall looks ridiculous; too little and the water will not run. Offer up the downpipe (or running) outlets and to each connect a plumb-line (a building line with a weight on the end). Locate the end of the plumb-line over the gulley and screw the running outlet into place on the fascia. Remove the line that gives you the fall and fix it to the newly positioned outlet. Mark on the fascia along this line at one-metre intervals, the position of each fascia bracket. Make sure in each case that the centre of the bracket touches the line. Screw each bracket home. Offer up the lengths of gutter and mark the positions where connector brackets will be necessary, then screw these into position. Now we have assembled the bed of the gutter. It remains to clip the lengths of gutter into the clips. Use a hacksaw to cut the plastic guttering to the required length.

The downpipe has to be clipped to the facing brickwork by wall-plugging a convenient mortar joint and screwing the clip back to the brickwork. The downpipe will either end in a 'shoe' or it will be pointed into the gully with cement mortar. If you wish to end the downpipe in a water-butt, take the overflow from the butt into the gully. It is as well to

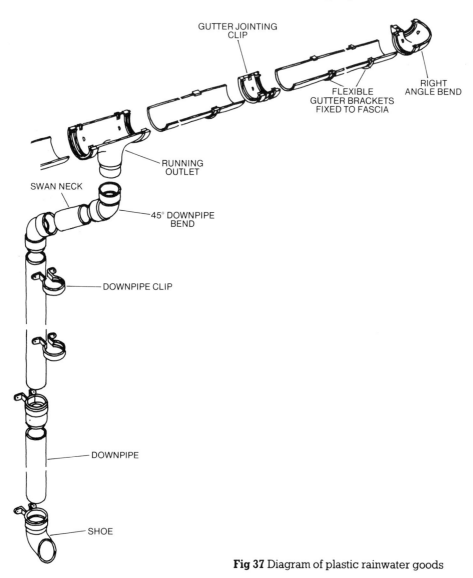

Fig 37 Diagram of plastic rainwater goods

try your gutter with buckets of water. You can solve any leaking joints so much more swiftly from the scaffold.

If all that works and there are no hideous cement blobs on the roof tiles, and the gables are neatly pointed and the chimneys have been bricked up above the ridge with 600mm (2ft) of facing brickwork and terminated with a pot or with a weathervane, or with a course of bricks corbelled out as a feature, and all the leadwork around the chimneys has been completed by the plumber to his and your and the building inspector's satisfaction – if all this has been achieved, and the scaffold is not to be used by the glazier, then the scaffold may be dismantled. Note that it is not necessary to terminate the chimney with a chimney pot; you can 'flaunch' or fill in around the last liner with cement mortar with the aim of directing rain water away from the flue and out over the brickwork of the chimney.

To dismantle the scaffold, drop the boards to the lift below and standing on this undo the bolts above you and pass the tubes to the ground. Repeat until you reach ground level, taking the utmost care as the scaffolding structure becomes more and more unstable as you remove its components.

The supply and fixing of glass is so competitively priced that this is a job the self-builder should most definitely put out to subcontractors. Generally, you will need 5mm thick clear glass, except where double glazing is the priority. The contractor will measure up every window. If your entrance doors have glass get them glazed before they are hung.

When the scaffolding company have hauled away their equipment, you can tidy the site once more, all the while admiring the safe, dry house. If you hang the external doors, you will have a safe, dry, lockable house secure against the elements and against thieves.

# 6
# FIRST FIX

All the time we are building there is the pressing worry of finance. Every move one makes will be haunted by the overdrawn balance. Each time-consuming, back-breaking task will be made that much less bearable by the croaking cormorant on your shoulder. There is, always, the dichotomy between forging ahead oneself, fulfilling dreams and crossing thresholds of personal endeavour, and enabling the project to survive without a yoke of extra debt. The 'first fix' phase of your building falls safely and achievably within the grasp of the self-builder. Here, more than anywhere, he can make his mark. First fixing in all trades does require extreme care and method, but it is the craftsmanship of the second fixing that gives your house the stamp of quality.

The term 'first fix' means, literally, the first attempt to fix basic items to the inside of the building in preparation for the plasterer. The trades involved are the carpenter, the electrician and the plumber. Each trade is concerned with laying the foundations to their respective end products. If you choose to use subcontractors then it is often a blessing to have them on site together so that problems affecting all trades may be mutually worked out. The whole of the first fix stage is reaching towards the moment when the plasterers step, languidly, on to the site. The management of the site becomes more hectic from now until completion, and the value of the materials used increases alarmingly.

Your house is dry but very dark. You need some form of temporary lighting. In the site hut we have a temporary power supply from which we can run an extension lead to the building to provide a string of lights. It is surprising just how much light the unfinished walls absorb, and I have used a portable lighting system which can be carried from room to room. Build out of 50mm × 25mm (2in × 1in) sawn batten an easel on to which you fix a second-hand fluorescent strip light. This is plugged into an extension lead and placed wherever the need for extra light arises.

All the tasks concerned with first fixing may be carried out simultaneously, but I shall treat the items discussed under each heading in the order in which I would approach them. You may choose to deal with the carpentry side yourself while engaging subcontractors for the electrical installation and the plumbing. In this event, the electrician and plumber may be forging ahead with their work alongside you, the carpenter. If at all possible you should be on site every day. A large number of fundamental decisions will be made by each tradesman and queries will arise.

## Upstairs Flooring

As a carpenter, first you must lay the flooring on the first floor to provide access to every room. All herringbone strutting must therefore be completed. Any trimming of the first floor joists around chimney breasts and stair wells must be satisfactorily finished. Tie a ladder to a convenient joist within the stair well to allow access to the first floor. If you have chosen chipboard sheet flooring then you will find 2440mm × 600mm (8ft × 2ft) sheets available at your local builders' merchant. These sheets are tongued and grooved so that a high standard of joint may be achieved. The thickness of the board will depend on the spacing of the joists. We have gone for a spacing of 406mm (16in), you will remember, to suit the plasterboard dimensions, and for this span the thickness should be 18mm (¾in). The properties of wood particle boards are contained in BS 2604. Do specify that you want 'flooring grade' chipboard when ordering.

Each sheet covers 1.4m². Haul the sheets up on to the joists. Carefully, still using your scaffold board walkways, start laying the sheets across the joists, ensuring that the joins coincide with a joist. Nail each board, along each joist (it may be necessary to pencil a line across the board to indicate the exact position of each joist), at 200mm (8in) centres. Drive the tongues and grooves together with great care. Use a batten and tap each joint home with a hammer. Leave a 10mm (⅜in) gap around the edge of the room to allow for expansion. If you are running heating pipes along the top of the joists you must leave a 'trap' which can be screwed down after the plumber has finished. If a joint between two boards occurs away from a joist it is necessary to provide noggins to give the joint support, eg where the joist end meets the perimeter wall. For all flooring use 50mm (2in) lost-head nails as these will drive home, satisfactorily burying their heads beneath the surface of the board.

If you need to cut a 'trap' after the floor had been nailed down, cut through the board along the side of a joist. Remove the board that will provide the access and nail noggins along the joists on either side of the opening. Then you can screw down the trap on to the noggin beams.

The windows must be glazed by this point, as rain water quickly destroys chipboard. Chipboard is easily cut with a handsaw, or better still with a Skilsaw. As soon as you have finished one room, set up a bench on which you can comfortably cut the boards for the rest of the first floor.

## Stairs

Four weeks before you begin the flooring you should have invited three joinery firms on to the site to measure up and to quote for the stairs. The construction of the stairs is a specialist job, treading through minefields of legislation and standards, and should not be undertaken unless you can achieve a very high standard of workmanship. The joinery men are conversant with the Building Regulations and will make a flight of stairs to suit your house. The dimensions they need are: the distance from the point vertically below the trimming joist, on which the stairs will rest, to the proposed bottom step of the stairs – this is called the 'going'; the distance from finished floor level on the ground floor to the top surface of the finished floor on the first floor – this is the 'rise'. Equipped with these measurements plus the plan, the joiner can work out a quotation, and if successful, may construct the perfect stairway for your house. It may be possible to arrive at ceiling heights that will perfectly suit 'ready-made stairs' from a joinery manufacturer.

We are interested here in 'private stairways' for domestic use and the criteria which govern the minimum requirements of stairways are to be found in the 1985 Building Regulations 'Stairways, Ramps and Guards'. A brief explanation of the terminology is necessary:

*Riser*: The vertical part of a stair, housed into the tread above and the

**Fig 38** Diagram of two types of stairs

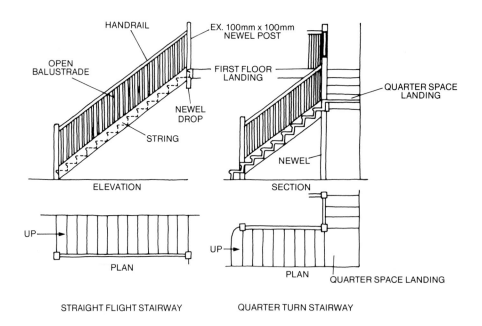

HANDRAIL

EX. 100mm x 100mm
NEWEL POST

OPEN
BALUSTRADE

FIRST FLOOR
LANDING

QUARTER SPACE
LANDING

NEWEL
DROP

STRING

NEWEL

ELEVATION

SECTION

UP

UP

PLAN

PLAN

QUARTER SPACE LANDING

STRAIGHT FLIGHT STAIRWAY

QUARTER TURN STAIRWAY

108

tread beneath. It must not be more than 220mm (8¾in). Risers are made of 14mm wood or 9mm plywood.

*Tread*: The horizontal member, housed into both strings. It must be not less than 235mm (9¼in) wide (see BS585, 1972, 'Wood Stairs'). They are made of 20mm (¾in) wood and have a rounded 'nose'.

*Strings*: Two side, supporting members of stairway, housed 12mm (½in) deep to receive both trends and risers. One string is usually fixed to a wall. The minimum thickness is 27mm (1⅛in).

*Newel*: Supports the handrail. It is morticed to the string and bolted to the trimmer joist on the landing. The minimum dimension is 75mm × 75mm (3in × 3in).

*Handrail*: Fixed to the newels. Minimum height above 'pitchline' is 840mm (33in). Runs parallel to pitchline.

*Balustrade*: Prime function is safety. The maximum distance between balusters (or banisters) is 90mm (3½in). The panelled balustrade is an alternative to banisters.

*Going*: The distance measured from face of riser to face of riser, a minimum of 220mm (8¾in).

*Nosing*: The projection over the riser of the step beneath it, equal to the thickness of the tread, ie 20mm (¾in).

*Rise*: The measurement from top of tread to top of tread. It must be not more than 220mm. The number of risers in any one flight should not exceed 15 (BS585, 'Wood Stairs').

*Pitch*: The angle between the pitch line and the floor must not exceed 42°.

A guiding principle which must be applied to your stairway, and will be by the joiner, is set out in BS585. It states that the sum of the 'going' of a step plus twice its rise must be between 550mm (22in) and 700mm (28in).

Study your Approved Document 'K', on page three of which there is a straightforward guide to the recommendations. Do not forget that the Building Regulations are concerned with the correct application of energy conservation, health and safety.

There is one other major requirement that has to be met, and that is the headroom measured from the pitch line of the stairway to the floor above. You must have 2m (6ft 6in) of clear space, measured vertically from the landing or floor above to the pitch line. Imagine dropping a plumb-line from the landing (or trimmer) on to the stairway. Measure the headroom from the point where the plumb bob touches the pitch line (the pitch line connects the noses of all the treads). Also we have to obtain a minimum distance of 1.5m (4ft 10½in) taken at right angles to the pitch line, across to the landing or first floor above.

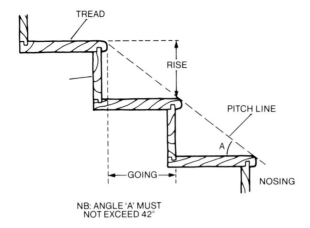

NB: ANGLE 'A' MUST
NOT EXCEED 42°

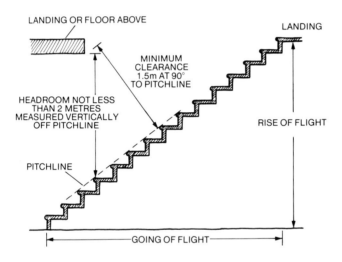

**Fig 39** Diagram to show characteristics of stairs and to name the components

Read carefully the Building Regulations Approved Document 'K' concerning stairways; it is a difficult area. It is impossible to make a stairway 'fit' once it is wrongly made, but on-site consultation with the joiner should ensure a perfect fit.

Once the stairs are delivered, they can be lifted into position and packed off the concrete subfloor. Somehow you have to imitate the finished floor level, otherwise the bottom riser will be buried in the screed and will not have the same rise as the rest. Every riser must be the same within a flight and every tread must have the same 'going' within a flight. The top riser fits against the landing trimmer so that the landing chipboard runs into the back of the nosing that forms the top step. The string that sits against the wall must be screwed to the masonry using

110

appropriate wallplugs or perhaps even 'Rawlbolts', following closely the manufacturer's instructions for fixing. If the underside of the stairs is filled in with studwork, this will provide extra support for the string which represents the outside of the stair. This applies to the simplest of stairways, called a 'straight flight', which consists of no more than fifteen treads and risers giving access to an upper floor. If a change of direction is required within the stairway, then a quarter landing or a winder may be fitted into the plan. In either case you may need advice on fixing, and the joiner who constructs the stairs may assist. The fixing of the newel posts is especially tricky, while the nailing of the balustrades once the handrail is in position, is simple.

As soon as the stairs are in position, be sure to cover them in polythene, and on each tread and riser carefully nail pieces of protective hardboard, rough side up. It may be wise to leave the newels and balustrades until after plastering. Remember, plasterers use large quantities of water, drop cement mortar everywhere and tread heavily.

## Door Linings

The next job in line for the carpenter is the fixing of all the internal door linings. These are constructed of softwood and 'line' the openings. They provide something on which to hang the door and create a surface which can be decorated.

In the case of door openings in masonry walls, you will remember we built the opening around a template, the external dimensions of which were a fraction greater than the proposed standard door lining. The lining must be designed to accept a door size which will have been worked out at the design stage. Let us assume you have chosen a door size of 762mm × 1,981mm (2ft 6in × 6ft 6in); you have to construct a lining consisting of two uprights and a head piece with an internal dimension of 766mm × 1,985mm (the extra width allows for clearance). The head must be grooved out to receive the uprights. The lining will be made from softwood boards measuring 138mm (5½in) by 25mm (1in) thick. The timber will be listed by the merchants as 'ex 32mm', which means that it has been machined from a rough sawn board measuring 32mm in thickness, but after the process of machining or planing it will finish up at a thickness of 25mm, the rest being lost as shavings. The width of material (138mm in the case) is vital as this allows for the plaster coats on both sides of wall in which the opening is located. If the width is too great, the plaster will be excessively thick; if the width is too small, the plaster cover will be too thin and you may have trouble in adequately burying electric cables. If you have used a standard 100mm (4in) internal lightweight block for the cross walls then a 138mm lining will give 19mm (¾in) of plaster cover on both sides of the wall, which is adequate.

On stud partitions constructed of timber, which we shall tackle in a moment, you will need thinner lining material because they will be fixed to a 100mm (4in) wooden upright or stud with 9mm (⅜in) plasterboard on either side, making an overall thickness for the partition of 127mm (5in). It is possible to purchase door lining sets from a builders' merchant but you must be sure the dimensions suit your openings. Once you have assembled the sets, the corners must be strongly braced to keep the lining square while you are fixing it in position. One of the great blessings attached to lightweight insulation blocks is the ease with which you can fix items to them. In the case of linings it is possible to use wire cut nails of an appropriate length, perhaps 75mm (3in), driven home so that the head is flush with the surface of the wood. Mark a line down the centre of the lining and nail along the line, which will later be covered by the doorstep. There is no need to try to fix the head piece. Insert pieces of wood behind the lining to counteract any tendency of the wood to twist during fixing. The foot of the lining can be buried in the screed.

## Stud Partitions

Any partition walls constructed of timber studwork can be built at this stage, using our new floor upstairs or off the concrete oversite on the ground floor. Whenever possible you should try to use masonry partitions as they offer the best sound insulation. In cases of partitions at first floor level which run with the joists as opposed to across the joists, it is necessary to double up the first floor joists to bear the partition adequately.

Timber stud partitions derive their name from the vertical timber members or 'studs' which are fixed at 406mm (16in) centres to suit 9mm (⅜in) thick plasterboards and at 610mm (24in) centres to suit 12mm (½in) plasterboards. The studs are nailed to a 'head' timber and to a 'sole plate' at the floor level. Through the middle of the partition must be fixed a line of nogging pieces to give extra stability to the studs. All timber used should be 100mm × 50mm (4in × 2in) rough sawn. It is good practice, and deserves a red star for effort, to cut notches in the sole plate and the head timber to receive the studs. Do not clad the partitions in plasterboard until all the first fix wiring is complete. The timber destined for studwork needs to be treated with preservative but it need not be stress graded.

## Window Boards

Another satisfying task, once all the studwork is complete, is to cut and fix all the window boards (internal window sills) into position. The window boards are, of necessity, wide enough to cover the cavity, the inner leaf and to project over the plaster line by 50mm (2in). You can use

112

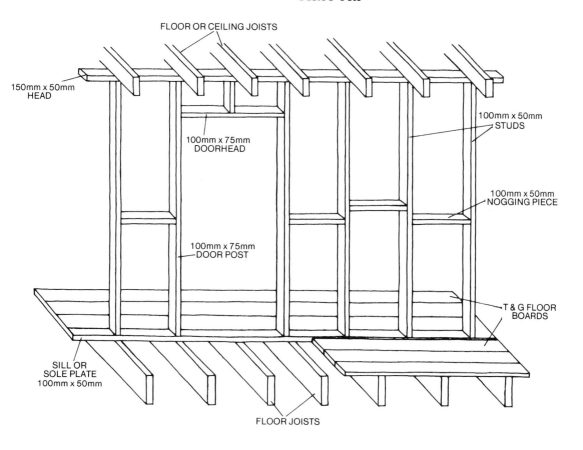

FLOOR OR CEILING JOISTS

150mm x 50mm
HEAD

100mm x 75mm
DOORHEAD

100mm x 50mm
STUDS

100mm x 50mm
NOGGING PIECE

100mm x 75mm
DOOR POST

T & G FLOOR
BOARDS

SILL OR
SOLE PLATE
100mm x 50mm

FLOOR JOISTS

**Fig 40** Diagram of a stud partition

a wood called Parana pine, which is widely available in 225mm (9in) widths and which is machined with a tongue on the back edge to locate the board into the rebate or groove provided in the window frame. The ideal position is to have the inner skin of blockwork finishing at just the right height under the window to allow the board to rest on the block-work at the same time as sliding into the rebate. We have previously sung praises to the properties of lightweight insulation blocks and once again their performance is superb. You can drill and countersink wood screws into the window board and using wallplugs firmly screw down the board. Another way to approach this problem is to mark a pencil line along the point where the blocks touch the board. Remove the board and hammer four wire staples into the underside of the board on the pencil line (woodscrews will suffice). Then twist lengths of galvanised wire around the staples. Drive into the blockwork four wire cut nails vertically below the staples; reset the board into the rebate and loop the wires around the corresponding cut nails. Using another cut nail as a

'Spanish windlass' tighten the wire as much as possible. The heads of the cut nails must not project from the wall face more than 19mm (¾in), and the whole affair will be buried in the plaster. This method helps to prevent cracking as the timber board dries out and lifts away from the plaster. Do not forget when ordering the window boards to allow, in each window, enough length for the board to run past the reveal of the opening by about 75mm (3in) each side.

## Curtain Track Fixings

The building is really beginning to shape up. All partition walls are formed; door linings are firmly in place; the stairs are in and covered. Soon we can summon the plasterer. After completing the window boards we might consider some provision for fixing curtain track. Catnic lintels are provided with clips which, most ingeniously, accept 50mm × 25mm (2in × 1in) batten. These blocks can be located vertically in three places across the face of the lintel; these positions should be recorded for swift retrieval after plastering. It is wise to place one batten at the centre of each window and one at each end, 225mm (9in) in from the reveal. If you apply this rule to every opening you should easily find all the fixings.

## Windows and Joinery

While on the subject of windows, we should focus on the construction of standard windows. A window is a joinery item. A joiner works at a bench in a joiner's shop and is concerned with producing specialist components for the building industry. Windows are standardised and are produced largely by specialist companies at much cheaper prices than would other-wise be charged by joiners making individual windows for individual buildings. It is worth collecting as many joinery catalogues as you can find in order to familiarise yourself with the products that are available. Most windows follow a standard pattern and size and there are a host of designs to choose from, each with different methods of repelling the weather. I have included a sketch of a standard window illustrating the construction of a window and naming the components (Figure 14).

A task that may be tackled by a plasterer is the fixing of all the plaster-board in the building. Very often this is carried out by site carpenters or skilled handymen and most certainly could be accomplished by a self-builder. It comes under the heading of first fix and is unquestionably leading towards the day the plasterer comes.

## Plasterboard

Plasterboard is manufactured in the Midlands by British Gypsum. Gypsum ($CaSO4.2H_2O$) is a naturally occurring mineral within the Triassic geological system. It is mined or quarried and the ore is crushed and heated to drive off the water of crystallisation. When mixed with water the powder sets very rapidly. Plasterboard is a sandwich of gypsum between two sheets of cardboard. We are concerned with two thicknesses: 9.5mm (⅜in) board is used for ceilings while 12.7mm (½in) boards are used for forming partitions. These sizes and uses are interchangeable but generally in a domestic dwelling the 9.5mm thickness is most widely used. The sheets come in a variety of dimensions but only two need concern us. The largest size produced for house building measures 2,438mm × 1,200mm (8ft × 4ft). The sheet will have one 'grey' side with a rough texture to receive plaster finishes and one 'ivory' or white side, which may be prepared and decorated as it stands. There is a smaller size on the market called a plasterboard lath, which measures 1,219mm × 914mm (4ft × 3ft) or 1,219mm × 406mm (4ft × 1ft 4in).

If you have a friend to help you, I would use the 2,438mm × 1,200mm × 9.5mm boards on the ceilings (but if gang nailed roof trusses are present at 600mm centres then 12.7mm thickness is advisable). Tackle the upstairs first. Carry enough boards upstairs to do each room; arrange the temporary lighting; rummage in the site hut and bring forth your box of 25kg of 30mm (1¼in) × 2.6mm diameter galvanised plasterboard nails, two claw hammers and one 50mm × 25mm (2in × 1in) straight batten cut off exactly to 2,438mm (8ft). The batten will be most helpful while planning the job. Also, make up two enormous wooden props with a flat board at the top measuring 1,200mm (4ft) in length on a stout timber 'leg' cut to the clear height of the rooms. Once you have fitted the board into position you can jam the two props firmly under it to pinch it against the ceiling joists. Assuming we are aiming for a high-quality plastered ceiling, as against Artex, which is applied with a brush, we fix the plasterboard grey side down, leaving a 5mm gap between boards. The boards must be nailed every 150mm (6in) along all the joists, keeping the nails as far in from the edge as possible. Drive the nails home but do not fracture the paper and try not to cover the ceiling in 'half-crowns' (where the hammer leaves its round mark). When stacking plasterboard it must be supported every 600mm (2ft) if on the oversite concrete and it must be absolutely dry. If you intend to decorate straight on to the plasterboard then you should order bevelled edge boards; these make light of the task of filling the joints, which can either be 'taped over' or just decorated. If you are on your own and can find no friends with a penchant for lifting heavy boards above their heads, you can use plasterboard laths throughout. Some say that the use of smaller boards provides a straight ceiling with less subsequent cracking as the timber dries out.

Do not forget that all the electrical wiring must be installed on the ground floor before you nail up a single board. The first floor can be reached from the roof space via the trap hatch which, incidentally, needs a 'lining' before plastering. Use some 75mm × 25mm (3in × 1in) prepared timber and construct a lining in situ, nailing each timber to the joists and trimmers, allowing the lining to project below the joists by 9.5mm, the thickness of the plasterboard, plus 4mm (⅛in) for the thickness of the finished plaster coat. All the time while installing linings you must be conscious of the finished thickness of plaster or what ever follows.

One final effort must be made to set up the building for plastering. At each window and door opening we have the reveals to worry about. How are we going to guarantee the correct thickness of plaster on each corner? How are we going to gauge the depth of plaster on each reveal? You have two options: traditionally you could use battens nailed on the inside surface of the opening while protruding over the wall face by 19mm. These are then reversed to form the guide for the reveal surfaces. The modern method, however, has the advantages of being permanent and in building extra strength into your corners. To follow this course you need the appropriate number of lengths of 'expamet' plaster bead (ref 563), available in individual lengths of 2,400mm (8ft) or 3,000mm (10ft). Take the angle bead, as it is often called, and cut it to length with a hacksaw (or tin snips). Nail it to the corners and top edge, if appropriate, with plasterboard nails. You will notice straight away that it gives both a key to hold the plaster and a depth gauge. On corners and reveals which will only receive the top coat of plaster, such as openings in studwork, fix 'expamet' thin-coat angle bead (ref 553), again using plasterboard nails. Do make sure that the angle bead is 'plumb' or upright. Use a spirit level to ensure that the plastered reveals will be perfect.

**Fig 41** Examples of plasterers angle bead designed to reinforce corners and to provide a depth gauge

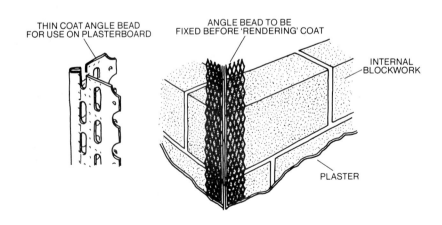

THIN COAT ANGLE BEAD
FOR USE ON PLASTERBOARD

ANGLE BEAD TO BE
FIXED BEFORE 'RENDERING' COAT

INTERNAL
BLOCKWORK

PLASTER

## Electrician

Now let us consider the electrical wiring at the first fix stage. This encompasses everything that will be buried by the plaster or covered by the plasterboard, and involves the fundamental layout of the whole wiring system. Electrics is a very exact science and is covered by labarinthine regulations for our own safety. I wired my own house to the approved standard; the installation was checked and tested by an electrical engineer and further tested by the power company before they would connect us to the main supply. You may wish to follow this route or to subcontract the whole installation. At this stage of the building procedure you can, very cheaply, build in twentieth-century features such as television aerial points in every room, telephone points, alarm systems, hi-fi lines and many more light and plug sockets than would normally be provided. You can think ahead to outdoor lighting schemes and actually lay the armoured cable to the coal-bunker, barbecue, greenhouse or Elizabethan knot garden. You can imagine which room will be used as a nursery and incorporate a baby alarm system to the master bedroom and to the kitchen. You can thread hi-fi wiring to every downstairs room. You can make provision for VHF aerials to reach exactly to the required position. You can build in provision for recessed lighting in the kitchen and for concealed cupboard lights, and for spotlights on sophisticated ceiling tracks. All this can be planned and dreamt about for many happy hours and can very cheaply be added to the building at the first fix stage. It will cost £35 to add a TV point in a room that has already been plastered and decorated.

When laying out an electrical system it is most helpful if the person who will use it is present: the self-builder can be both designer and user. There are some general points that are helpful, followed by the requirements laid down by the regulations, which must be met. The general points to consider are such things as building in flexibility to allow for change of use in a room. Remember that power points should be positioned in diametrically opposed corners and in so doing feed between them the whole room. Build in two-way switching on stairways, long corridors and across long rooms with doors at either end and between porch lights and kitchen lights. Two-way switching is the facility to switch the same light on and off at two different switching positions.

The ultimate legislation covering all aspects of the provision of electrical energy is found under Regulation 26 of the 1937 Electrical Supply Regulations, which have been amended and updated until, in 1985, we find the fifteenth edition in operation. The Institution of Electrical Engineers (IEE) is the body responsible for producing and updating the electrical regulations. The regulations are there to protect us; as the requirements become more stringent so we become more safe.

There is a guide to the fifteenth edition of the IEE wiring regulations written by J. F. Whitfield, which is very clear and useful. At the end of the wiring task and before the power company will connect your building to the mains supply, you are obliged to fill out a form entitled the Completion of Installation Advice. This stipulates various stringent tests to be applied to the whole system and is best carried out by an approved electrical contractor, approved that is by the National Inspection Council for Electrical Installation Contracting. He will carry out the tests and prove your system to be safe before signing the test sheet. He will be perfectly prepared to carry out the tests having not actually installed the system. The following attempts to make clear the requirements of the IEE wiring regulations as they affect a dwelling.

The power supply will come to the building overhead or, let us hope, underground. If it comes underground then ducting will have been provided by you to a position, as agreed with the representative of the power company, where the meter will be fixed. The modern tendency is to fit a very ugly white meter box into the cavity wall to enable the meter to be read by the power company from the outside of the building at any time. The incoming power cable which is provided by the power company will pass up a plastic conduit called a 'hockey stick', which is housed in the cavity. The provision of the meter box, hockey stick and incoming cable, plus the connecting of the meter, is all the responsibility of the power company. They will not undertake this until the wiring of the building has passed its test. You are responsible for providing all the equipment and cables from the meter position throughout the house. So working from the meter position upwards, as it were, we shall encounter a live and a neutral terminal which must be a minimum of 16mm$^2$ in cross-sectional area and which will eventually connect the meter to the consumer unit. There will also be an earth wire which must be not less than 16mm$^2$ in area, connecting the earth terminal of the consumer unit to the earth point at the meter position. The consumer unit is a plastic or metal box containing six, eight, twelve or twenty-four live terminals and the same number of neutral terminals, from which the incoming power may be distributed to all the positions in the building.

The consumer unit incorporates the protection of the system in the form either of fuses or miniature circuit breakers (MCBs). The safety protection offered by the fuses saves the system from current overload caused by turning on too many appliances at once or using an appliance that demands too high a current. The surge across the fuse causes the weakest part of the circuit to break. This can still be done with rewirable fuses, but has been replaced by much safer high rupturing capacity (HRC) cartridge fuses. You can still use rewirable fuses, but it is possible that in order to satisfy the regulations you may be obliged to increase the sizes of the current-carrying conductors in the cable. There are on the market consumer units where the overload protection is provided by MCBs, referred to above, which have switches enabling you to reconnect the system, after failure, more easily.

The additional protection the system needs is against a failure in the wiring or in an appliance, causing current to flow along the earth wires. This is intercepted at the consumer unit by an earth leakage protection circuit breaker, which very rapidly cuts off the supply of current. This system of earth leakage protection is in addition to the supply company's earthing arrangements, and would be absolutely required where the company could not provide an earth facility. The equipment used for this purpose is called a residual current circuit breaker (RCCB) and each terminal on the consumer unit or sections of the unit may be protected separately, so that if there is an appliance leaking to earth on a particular circuit then only that affected circuit will cut out. It is possible either to protect the whole installation or each individual circuit. A consumer unit employing RCCBs is called an RCD (residual current device).

Other major requirements of the regulations are: the voltage drop in 240V must not exceed 6V; your system must not have lengths of cable more than 80m (260ft) in length; you should avoid grouping cables together because of the possibility of magnetic fields causing voltage drop; you must not run cables close to hot water pipes, for the same reason. Avoid laying cables under insulation material.

In a four-bedroom house you are going to need the following wiring circuits:

| | Size of cable (mm$^2$) |
|---|---|
| First floor ring main | 2.5 |
| Ground floor ring main | 2.5 |
| First floor lighting | 1 |
| Ground floor lighting | 1 |
| Immersion heater | 2.5 |
| Cooker | 6 |
| TV aerial | Coaxial cable |
| Telephone points | British Telecom |

The ring circuit supplies all the socket outlets in all the rooms on a particular floor, the cable linking one outlet to the next, and back to the consumer unit. The lighting circuits do the same; in the 'looping in' system live and neutral cables run from one light fitting to the next, the live element of the system being passed through a switch. All switches must be switched 'in the line'; you should not use junction boxes to distribute power to the lighting circuit. All connections must be made at the light fitting or switch whether it is a pendent, batten holder, or fluorescent strip light.

We now know what size of cable feeds each circuit. We know the position of every socket and fitting in the building from our ground floor and first floor plans, marked up with out final decisions gathered from hours of thought and calculation.

The first floor ring main must leave the consumer unit position and pass up to first floor joist level, where it may be threaded through 25mm holes drilled in the middle of the joist, as near to the load-bearing wall as possible so as not to weaken the joists. The cable must be clipped to the side of the joist where appropriate, making allowance for the nailing of the ceiling board and the floorboards which are already in place. Wherever there is a socket outlet the cable will pass up the wall in a conduit to the box position, and back down from the box in another conduit and then continues its travels to all other socket outlets on the first floor level. The socket outlet is mounted in a galvanised metal box with adjustable lugs, into which the face-plate of the socket outlet is screwed. The box must be not less than 150mm (6in) above the skirting board, higher if you wish. The cables running to and from any socket outlet must run in straight lines, vertically. They must be protected by conduit – the best is PVC oval conduit of 18mm (⅝in) diameter – and the conduit should be 'chased' into a shallow trench (cut in the wall) and nailed with pairs of plasterboard nails, as necessary, with the nail heads just pinching the tube. This will all be buried by the plaster. The conduit must pass into the outlet box, which is also 'chased' into the wall and nailed back with plasterboard nails. The conduit should finish 12mm above the joists when entering the roof space. If a cable has to come through a wall into the back of a socket outlet box then it must pass through a rubber grommet. The cables can be folded neatly into the socket box out of the way of the plasterer.

Now you can see clearly why we need a good depth of plaster. Traditionally there is 19mm (¾in) cover on the walls but modern buildings get away with less. Beware of too thin a cover on your electrical conduit or it may 'grin' through at you later and remind you of your skinflint approach. The socket boxes should finish flush with the plaster line. Be careful not to bury them too deeply because the screws that hold the face-plates are of a limited length.

The ground floor ring circuit must leave the consumer unit position and follow a course beneath the suspended timber floor, if you have one, or if you have a screed then up into the first floor joists whence it descends to each socket outlet position, two cables at a time each in oval conduit just as in the first floor circuit. Do keep the conduits vertical; do not traverse the wall horizontally to reach a socket outlet. The knock-out boxes, as they are called in the trade, must be nailed or screwed into their recessed 'chases' as previously described. You must strive to set these level because, although there is some adjustment on the movable lugs of the face-plate, it is not enough to compensate for badly positioned boxes. The face-plate must be dead level. These same rules apply to TV aerial fittings, telephone fittings and hi-fi terminals.

Switch sockets must be treated in precisely the same way. The height of the switches is a matter for you to decide. Where two-way switching is planned it is likely that you will need three core and earth cable (red, yellow and blue) between the two switch positions in question.

Go over your wiring diagrams and lists. Check and re-check that all the socket outlets are fixed; that all the lighting has been provided for; that the stud partitions are threaded with cable and that no cable is at risk from carpenter's nails. Have you provided a socket for the central heating circulation pump? Have you remembered the cooker cable? The cooker panel has its own box to be buried in the plasterwork which is treated in exactly the same way as all the other knock-out boxes. (They are called knock-out boxes because of the semi-cut holes at various points around the box to allow cables in from every direction. You simply 'knock out' the hole that corresponds with your particular demand). The 6mm$^2$ cable will need a special conduit.

When you are satisfied that everything has been considered and that all the equipment has been installed to the highest standard, you can begin to send smoke signals to the plasterer or, if you are to play the part of plasterer, you have earned a quiet rest in the site hut.

## Plumber

The plumber has two aspects of the installation to worry about at the first fix stage. One concerns the domestic plumbing to and from all sanitary ware and the other concerns the central heating. He must lay out the cold water pipework to all the cold taps in the building rising from the new service ducted into the kitchen and coming out of the floor under the sink. Whatever you do, insist on a 19mm (¾in) alkathene supply pipe from the main water authority stop-valve to the kitchen sink stop-valve. You have then taken a small precaution to provide a good water pressure no matter what may befall your area in the way of housing development and no matter how your own requirements may change. The plumber must link all the hot taps in the building to the hot cylinder, remembering that this supply is gravity fed and should have long runs in 19mm (¾in) copper pipework. In large houses with very long pipe runs a smaller diameter pipe may be required to improve draw-off and to comply with water authority byelaws. The kitchen sink hot tap, being on the ground floor, may be supplied by 15mm (½in) pipework. The pipes may have to be notched into the top of the chamber joists; be careful not to cut too deeply and always confine the notches to the ends of joists where they find their bearing. Do not attempt to bury pipes in the wall. Where pipes have to drop from one floor to the next they should be clipped to the plasterwork or blockwork and then boxed in with either plywood or plasterboard panels. Clip the pipes at intervals of a metre. The pipework may be terminated just below floor level (beneath a trap) or just above ceiling level – these short lengths are called 'tails'.

**Fig 42** Diagram of typical soil vent stack showing the vent through the roof

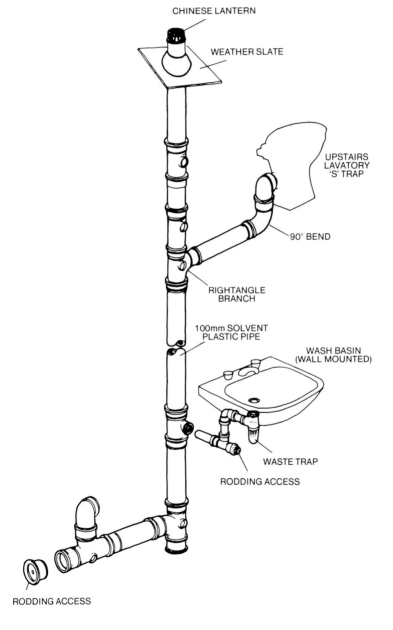

At this stage we can begin to build the soil vent pipe which proceeds from the ground floor entry of the drains up to the roof, where it must terminate 600mm (2ft) above the window heads on the first floor (heights are referred to in BS5572). The purpose of this is to ventilate the foul drainage system and to stop the syphoning of the traps on the lavatories. The soil vent stack is made of 100mm (4in) grey plastic pipe, which is available in long lengths complete with a wide range of bends, connectors and fittings to enable all the waste connections to empty into the stack. As this will be a candidate for boxing in, I should fix battens to the blockwork to form the basis of future cladding ideas and allow the plasterers to bring the finished plasterwork up to the batten. Make sure the battens are absolutely vertical.

For the central heating system the plumber must make provision for all the first floor pipework which will run through the chamber joists, and for all ground floor pipework, if a suspended floor is chosen. The boiler position must be established (rather in the same way as the meter position provided the basis for all electrical planning) and the radiator sizes and positions must be marked on the plan by this stage. How do we establish radiator sizes?

In order to calculate the output of the boiler and the number and size of radiators required we must take each room individually and work out the heat loss from that room. We also have to know the 'design temperature' of each room and the correct number of air changes per hour needed to make the room comfortable to inhabit. Figure 43B shows the general design temperatures that we might aim for.

Next we need to investigate U-values. These refer to a measurement of heat loss through a square metre of a given set of materials used in general construction. Every component of a building has been given a U-value; various combinations of components produce either a highly desirable position where the U-value is low, and this section of the building is considered to be thermally efficient because it is stoically resisting heat loss, or the components combine to give more rapid heat loss, which in this age of energy conservation is undesirable. The Building Regulations state that a U-value of $0.6W/M^2\,°C$ must be achieved on all external walls of a new building; which combination of materials you use to construct your cavity wall is up to you. It follows that all parts of the building carry there own U-values: a ceiling of plasterboard serving a ground floor room with a wooden floor above has a U-value of $1.7W/M^2\,°C$ in relation to heat loss upwards; a single-glazed window in a wooden frame has a U-value of 4.3; a ground floor of concrete covered with thermoplastic tiles has a U-value of 0.60; and so on. There are tables to cover every surface through which heat will be lost.

Having established design temperatures in each room we must take

**DESIGN CONDITIONS**

| Room | Design temp. °C | °F | Infiltration Air changes/h |
|---|---|---|---|
| Living, dining, bed-sitter | 21-24 | 70-75 | 1-2 |
| Kitchen | 18 | 65 | 2 |
| Hall, landing | 18 | 65 | 2 |
| Bedroom | 13-18 | 55-65 | 1 |
| Bathroom | 22 | 72 | 2 |
| Offices | 20 | 68 | 1-2 |

**Fig 43A** Design Conditions

**I.H.V.E. DESIGN TEMPERATURES**

| Room | 1965 air temperature | 1971 environmental temperature |
|---|---|---|
| Living room | 65°F | 21°C (70°F) |
| Dining room | 65°F | 21°C (70°F) |
| Bed-sitter | 65°F | 21°C (70°F) |
| Hall | 60°F | 16°C (61°F) |
| Bedroom | 60°F | 18°C (65°F) |
| Bathroom | 70°F | 22°C (72°F) |
| Toilet | 60°F | 18°C (65°F) |

| Room | Heat Loss | |
|---|---|---|
| | W | Btu/h |
| Dining | 1880 | 6710 |
| Lounge | 2020 | 6890 |
| Hall | 1730 | 5910 |
| Kitchen | 1450 | 4950 |
| Bedroom 1 | 1680 | 5730 |
| Bedroom 2 | 1770 | 6040 |
| Bedroom 3 | 880 | 3010 |
| Bathroom | 1400 | 4780 |
| Upper Hall | 770 | 2630 |
| Totals | 13580 | 46650 |

**Fig 43B** I.H.V.E. Design Temperatures

into account the temperature difference from room to room, which will increase the heat loss from a room above the factor of the U-value. For example, if a dining room with a design temperature of 21°C was to be situated next to a kitchen with a design temperature of 18°C, then when calculating the heat loss for the dining room you would have to multiply by a temperature difference of 3°C.

To recapitulate, we have a design temperature of a room to try and achieve with our new heating system, which is working against 'heat loss'. The rate of heat loss is dependent upon ventilation or the number of air changes per hour, upon the U-value of the materials enclosing the rooms, and upon the temperature differential between the adjoining rooms and the room in question. All this to discover the size of a radiator – but if you have not yet decided to contact your nearest heating engineer, let us press on.

Next, we must break down the surfaces in the room to determine heat loss accurately through each, by considering the external surfaces of floor and wall minus window, and the internal surfaces of ceilings and partition walls between other rooms and the room in question. The temperature difference between the external walls and the outside will be expressed as the difference between the ambient temperature at 0°C and the design temperature of the room.

The formula may be expressed as follows: the sum of the areas of each wall, ceiling and floor in square metres multiplied by the U-value of each wall gives the heat loss per degree Celsius in watts per metre; this, multiplied by the temperature difference between rooms or between the

**Fig 43C** U Valves

| U VALUES | | |
|---|---|---|
| Element | Construction | Standard W/m² °C |
| External wall | 220mm (9 in) solid brick plastered one side | 2.1 |
| | 335mm (13½ in) solid brick plastered one side | 1.7 |
| | 260mm (11 in) unventilated cavity brick, plastered one side | 1.5 |
| | 260mm (11 in) unventilated cavity, 105mm brick and 100mm insulating block plastered one side | 1.0 |
| Partition walls | 220mm (9 in) brick plastered both sides | 1.7 |
| | 110mm (4½ in) brick plastered both sides | 2.3 |
| | 75mm (3 in) breeze plastered both sides | 2.2 |
| Doors | 25mm (1 in) wood, or cored | 2.4 |
| Windows | Single-glazed windows: | |
| | Wooden frames | 4.3 |
| | Metal frames | 5.6 |
| | Double glazed windows: (Air space 20mm or more) | |
| | Wooden frames | 2.5 |
| | Metal frames | 3.2 |
| Ground floor | Ventilated wood floor on joists, air brick one side | 0.7 |
| | Solid concrete with thermoplastic tiles | 0.60 |
| | Solid concrete with wood block | 0.56 |
| Intermediate floor | Wood floor on joists: | |
| | Heat flow up | 1.7 |
| | Heat flow down | 1.5 |
| Pitched roof | Plaster ceiling, roof space above: | |
| | Uninsulated | 2.1 |
| | Foil-backed plasterboard to ceiling | 1.5 |
| | 25mm (1 in) mineral wool | 0.8 |
| | 50mm (2 in) mineral wool | 0.5 |

room and the outdoor temperature, gives the total heat loss in watts. You will have to install radiators to combat that heat loss and to maintain your design temperatures. The radiator should where possible be positioned under a window in order to maximise the convection of hot air across the room. If you have to position radiators against walls you must add a radiator shelf on top to deflect the hot air, and to stop dust marks appearing on the paintwork above the radiator. Always purchase 'high-output convector radiators', which produce the most heat from the smallest appliance. Here is a heat loss calculation example:

**HEAT LOSS CALCULATIONS     SI UNITS**

| Room and building element | Dimensions m | Area m² | U-value W/m² °C | Heat loss per °C W | Temp. diff. °C | Heat loss W |
|---|---|---|---|---|---|---|
| DINING (21°C, 2 air changes/h) | | | | | | |
| Air change | 3.7 x 5.5 x 2.4 | 48.8 (m³) | 0.66* | 32.2 | | |
| Floor | 3.7 x 5.5 | 20.4 | 0.7 | 14.3 | | |
| Wall | 3.7 x 2.4 | 8.9 | – | – | | |
| Window | 1.8 x 1.2 | 2.2 | 5.6 | 12.3 | | |
| Nett wall | | 6.7 | 1.0 | 6.7 | | |
| | | | | 65.5 | 22 | 1441 |
| Losses through internal surfaces: | | | | | | |
| Party wall (13°C) | 5.5 x 2.4 | 13.2 | 1.7 | 22.4 | 8 | 179 |
| Kitchen wall (18°C) | 5.5 x 2.4 | 13.2 | 2.2 | 29.1 | 3 | 87 |
| Ceiling (16°C) | 3.7 x 5.5 | 20.4 | 1.7 | 24.7 | 5 | 173 |
| | | | | | TOTAL | 1880 W |

**Fig 44A** Heat Loss Calculations

With a clear knowledge of each radiator position and the overall size of each radiator, you must now look for the most straightforward route to supply each radiator with a flow and a return pipe. It is not sufficient to run a single pipe past each radiator with two 'T' pipes connecting to the two valves. There must be two 15mm supply pipes with one radiator valve connected to the flow pipe and the other valve connected to the return pipe. You will need a flow and return circuit for the first floor and a separate circuit for the ground floor. All concealed pipes must be insulated with the best pipe insulation on the market. In the roof space there must be a small independent header tank, supplied by its own ball valve from the cold water mains. The purpose of this small reservoir is to top up the water in the radiator circuit. The header tank should also be

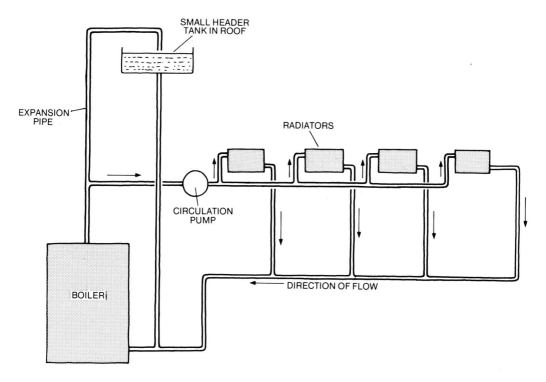

SMALL HEADER
TANK IN ROOF

EXPANSION
PIPE

RADIATORS

CIRCULATION
PUMP

BOILER

DIRECTION OF FLOW

**Fig 44B** Diagram of two pipe flow and return central heating system

connected to the primary flow and return circuit feeding the hot water cylinder, for the same reason.

The bending of copper pipes, be they 22mm or 15mm, may be tackled with gusto by the self-builder, once in possession of a portable pair of pipe benders. They are obtainable from any good tool hire shop and come complete with formers to suit each size of pipe. Do not trouble with 'bending springs' which you insert down the pipe. The spring maintains the shape of the pipe but they can be extremely difficult to remove, the pipe having been bent. Practice with your 'pipe bender' on some off-cuts of tubing. At all times when installing runs of pipework strive for neatness: use plenty of pipe clips for support; space pairs of pipes in perfect parallel lines and keep them vertical when surface fixing is unavoidable.

# 7
# PLASTERING

The plastering is a most satisfying, most transforming stage. I should say it alters the 'dungeon' more than any other single operation. It is the quickest in terms of the ratio of achievement to effort. I tackled a good percentage of the blockwork surface myself, with the result that our eyes never experience complete 'flatness'. You do have to live with your plastering and with this in mind you may wish to contact a plastering subcontractor; try to find one through personal recommendation. The form which a specification should take, together with various useful guidelines, are given at the end of this chapter. Let us attempt the plastering first-hand for those intrepid builders who really wish to experience each trade.

## Preparation of the Site
The site must be absolutely ready to receive the plasterer (or yourself acting as plasterer) because the process of plastering must be a continuous, flowing activity. The external door frames into the building must have their jambs protected from damage by wheelbarrows. The entrance that is nearest the sand pile and mixer should be boarded out to form a comfortable ramp into and out of the building. Do not forget that twenty to twenty-five tons of wet mortar will be wheeled into the building and just under half will go upstairs. I suggest you start upstairs while enthusiasm is at a high level. Like other heavy building jobs already tackled this one is about logistics, ie the movement of tons of cement mortar into and all over the building to its final position, trowel by trowel, on to the wall. Your first attempts should be confined to a guest bedroom, where any extraordinary 'terracing' on the plastered walls will be less likely to inflict permanent psychological harm.

## Ingredients
The sand must be obtained from the nearest pit, as haulage is the main cost. The sand we require for plastering must be 'washed', that is to say rinsed thoroughly at source to remove chemical impurities, mud and clay. If you remember, the common building sand used in mortar for

bricks and blocks contained clay and natural impurities. Here we are faced with applying a ⅜in thickness to our walls and any stones in the sand are totally unacceptable. It is vital to make your order absolutely clear: ten tons of the wrong material is difficult to wish away. The sand should arrive on a ten-ton truck capable of backing to the mixer position (which should not alter throughout the building process).

The next ingredient is cement. The name given to the first coat of plaster is 'render'. The colour of the render coat or rendering is unimportant, and thus the particular brand of cement used can vary from the brand employed in the brickwork. I do not advise a change, however, because you might use it for pointing brickwork around flashings, overflow pipes, steps, garden walls, etc, and a different colour would shine out and mock you for evermore.

The other main ingredient is treated with great respect in the trade: it is called mortar plasticiser. This liquid takes the place of lime in modern plaster mixes and allows the material to flow off the trowel and stick to the wall. It is the same material used in mortar for brickwork and blockwork, but in this job it gives the washed sand the 'body' which it lacks. All it does is to mix air bubbles into the mortar and alter the nature of the sand and cement into a 'margarine'.

Now we have assembled all the heavy materials; the mixer is fueled up, the barrow is oiled, the planks are in place, we cannot delay any longer.

## Plastering Technique

Find a blockwork wall upstairs without openings. In order to apply a flat, even thickness of render you must have guidelines. 'A builder uses straight edges and rules' – these words ring in our ears – and here we apply this ancient principle again. Take 19mm × 38mm (¾in × 1½in) battens cut to the height of the room and cutnail these to the wall, keeping them vertical. Leave the cutnails proud to facilitate easy withdrawal later. Now you have a gauge to show you the thickness of the plaster, ie 19mm. Repeat this battening over the entire room at 2m (6ft 6in) centres. Then cut a piece of 75mm × 25mm (3in × 1in) batten at 2.2m (7ft 2in) to provide a screeding board which you can use between the 19mm × 38mm battens to scrape off excess mortar.

It is important to have some sort of table whose surface is 1,200mm (4ft) above the floor, on to which you can empty bucketfuls of mortar. The theory is that you might load up the table with four buckets of mortar before starting, so that you achieve perhaps fifteen minutes of uninterrupted plastering before recharging your table. Place the table in the centre of the room. Beside it you will need a bucket of clean water together with a soft, small-handled sweeping brush.

From the convenient table-top you can scrape mortar onto a 'hawk'. The hawk is a light wooden or plastic hand-held platform resembling a bird table. It provides a resting place for the mortar before it reaches the wall or slides, infuriatingly, into your boot. You carry the hawk to the wall, together with a steel plasterers' trowel or 'float' as it is often called, with which you must apply dollops of mortar, which should stick to the blockwork. If the blocks are too dry then flick some water on to them using the soft brush.

Let us concentrate on the stages of the mixing operation. Mix the mortar at a ratio of 6 : 1. Add 5ml of mortar plasticiser (Febmix) to each mixerful. Do not overfill the mixer. Make the mortar fairly wet so that it runs off the trowel and yet is stiff enough for you to be able to cut it. Fill the barrow and propel it to the bottom of the stairs. Load it into buckets and convey them to the high, level table. Carry out further mixing on the table with the trowel. Scoop the mortar on to the hawk. Hold the hawk near the wall surface and start placing trowelfuls of mortar on to the surface between the battens.

Having filled an area between two vertical battens, pause to screed off the work with the screeding board, using a slow, firm sawing motion from the bottom to the top, keeping a good pressure on the batten guides. Flick the surplus mortar from the board surface to the high table for re-use. Admire your first flat piece of rendering.

Once the room is complete remove the battens, perhaps the next day, and fill in the channels with fresh mortar. You are left with a 'screeded', rough-textured, flat surface. Where the blockwork is uneven, it is possible to hide this by packing off the battens to increase the thickness of plaster at a given point so as to hide the problem.

When the rendering is complete and the mixer breathes out its last carbony breath and silence falls, empty any remaining cement out of the paper bags into polythene sacks, exhaust the air and tie the necks. No more cementy thoughts for a while. The next job is where the real skill is to be found.

## The Finishing Coat

Your rendered walls are nice and flat. The upstairs will be drying out to a khaki roughness reminiscent of hair shirts; the ground floor will remain damp longer as air circulation is poor and the block walls will be wetter. On to this surface it is the intention to apply a thin 3mm (⅛in) coat of pink or grey gypsum plaster. Once more, head for the guest bedroom. Take the same high table, two buckets, your trowel, the soft sweeping brush, a few sweeping statements, your hawk and a bag of gypsum wall plaster weighing 50kg. The bag will bear the name Sirapite.

Modern building plasters are manufactured from gypsum as the raw material. This substance is mined and crushed and heated to 200°C. The purest material to come out of this process is plaster of Paris, which sets very rapidly. The next in line is retarded hemihydrate gypsum plaster, which has materials added to it to obstruct the rate of crystallisation and hence extend the drying time. The classification of plasters (BS1191) lists gypsum plasters as follows:

Class A   Plaster of Paris
Class B   Retarded hemihydrate gypsum plaster
Class C   Anhydrous gypsum plaster – Sirapite Thistle
Class D   Keene's or Parian plaster

The drying time is the critical factor. Thistle Board Finish is most useful for work on plasterboard and is usually grey in colour. Sirapite is most effective for finishing on top of rendering and is often pink. The freshness of both products is most important; the older the powder, the slower it sets. A plaster that sets too quickly does not give you time to smooth it out, whereas if it is too retarded you may be waiting all night to effect the finishing touches. This highlights the need to tackle the correct amount of wall at one time; you must be able to finish each section before the end of the day.

Begin by pouring into the first bucket about two pints of clean water. The whole of this operation must be clinically clean because the Sirapite will react disastrously with any impurities. Into this water sprinkle two or three trowelfuls (keep a dry garden trowel for scooping out the powder) of plaster and stir with a special whisk (a stick studded with 50mm (2in) nails, constructed by yourself, resembling a vicious medieval weapon). The powder will turn rapidly into a soup and more powder must be carefully sprinkled on to the surface until a thicker mixture is achieved. Too much powder and the mix is ruined. You cannot add more water to save the day. Throw away and start again. If, however, you succeed in producing a workable plaster in one move, you are a genius and should not be on a building site but in a chemistry laboratory. The correct consistency will creamily pour on to the table, maintaining a depth of 50mm (2in). This will enable you to scoop it cleanly and deftly on to the hawk, and thence on to the wall, making sweeping movements with the trowel to spread the material as evenly as possible over the surface. Attack a whole wall at once, but not more than one wall. Apply the plaster as fast as possible, trying to judge the mix in relation to the surface area. Then having covered the area, watch and wait as the surface dries. At this point, when it is tacky, take your soft brush and flick water on to your work. As you do so, pass the trowel over the surface pushing a bow wave of runny plaster ahead of it. You will see the smoothness gradually materialising as you continue to push the wave back and forth over the area. Allow to dry and then repeat using less water and more powerful trowel strokes, to achieve a polished, shiny surface with no trowel marks or ridges. This time you have no battens to indicate the thickness; it is simply the barest of coverings, but if the render is showing it is too thin.

## Plastering the Ceiling

The ceiling (boarded throughout as discussed in Chapter 6) is very difficult to plaster. You mix the plaster in a bucket as above, the difference being that this material is called Thistle Board Finish plaster and is usually grey. When doing the ceiling you must build a platform of scaffold planks to fill the room, the purpose being to arrive at a comfortable position with arms outstretched to apply trowelfuls of wet plaster. The platform can rest on empty oil drums or 18in × 9in × 4in lightweight celcon blocks.

Place your table on the boarded platform and work entirely from this level. Apply plaster evenly to all the joints between the boards. Cut and press lengths of linen scrim cloth into the wet plaster to reinforce the joint. Put the plaster on in the same way as for the walls and allow to dry. It will dry faster so it is important to watch the condition of the ceiling most carefully. Work it exactly like the wall surface. Artificial light is essential when doing the ceiling and a mobile fluorescent strip light on a tripod is very effective.

## Subcontracting

There is a simpler way around plastering. If it is the one task you cannot face; if you have heard tales in pubs of zombie-like do-it-yourself plasterers with prematurely grey hair due to the cruel gymnastics, then seek out a plastering gang. A team is advisable as they share out the work and they will complete the messy business in weeks, not months. Generally two plasterers and one labourer form the neatest unit; you and your neighbourhood may regret the passage of a larger gang. One has heard tell of frying kippers on shovels over fires made of roofing felt and damp cement bags – a secondary form of 'smoking' I suppose. Once in search of plasterers, you must really cover the ground. Phone your local small builder and enquire which firm they use. Try and see an example of their work or at least get a verbal recommendation. Try to obtain three estimates (as with everything else in building) and write down your requirements so that each man is quoting for exactly the same work. Your specification might look like this:

Apply one sound coat of ⅜in thick sand and cement render to all internal walls, reveals, etc, using washed plasterer's sand.

Apply one even coat of Sirapite plaster to all walls, reveals, etc, in accordance with modern practice.

Apply one coat of Thistle Board Finish to all ceilings. Scrim all plasterboard joints.

You are permitted to use plasterer's 'expamet' angle bead provided adequate fixings are used.

Supply all materials.

Clean the site each day.

Protect woodwork where necessary.

To be completed by . . .

When inviting subcontractors on to your building site, you must give them target dates. If you do not, the work will take ages and the building cannot begin to dry out until the plasterers vanish.

# 8
# SECOND FIX

Open plenty of windows whenever the elements allow it, to ventilate the building and dry the plaster. Make sure there are locks on the external doors, as the next phase involves expensive items which will be stored on the site.

**Suspended Ground Floors**
If this type of floor has been decided upon, it may be an advantage to lay it before the plastering, or you may be able to fit it into the schedule at this point. The lack of a finished floor while tackling the first fix may prove inconvenient, but on the other hand it will not be damaged by barrows, boots and heavy trestles. Also the plumber will be unrestricted with his long lengths of pipe. At Hancocks I laid the ground floor after the plastering and I think the freedom to stomp about on the oversite concrete outweighed the inconvenience of high thresholds and difficulties with the stairs.

**Fig 45** Diagram of a suspended timber floor showing ventilation

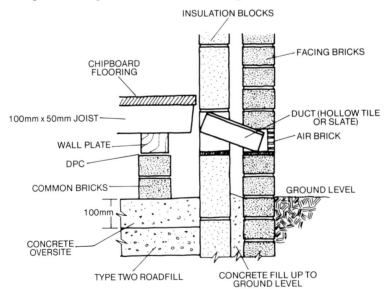

The concrete oversite in the case of a suspended timber floor must finish level with, or higher than, the adjacent ground level. A gap of 75mm (3in) must exist between the surface of the concrete and the underside of the wall-plate, and a gap of not less than 125mm (5in) must exist between the underside of the suspended joists and the surface of the concrete. On to this oversite concrete we build honeycomb brick walls (a single brick thick) at 2m (6ft 6in) centres, standing the outside honeycomb walls off the inner skin of the cavity wall by 100mm (4in). The damp-proof course to be laid on top of the honeycomb wall will line through with the damp-proof course on the external walls. Air bricks are provided in the external walls to ventilate the underfloor space. As the oversite concrete should be level, it is an easy task to build level, straight, dwarf walls.

Once the damp-proof course is in place we can lay 100mm × 75mm (4in × 3in) wall-plates but not, in this case, nailing them to the brickwork as we would puncture the nice new damp-proof course. On to the wall-plates we can lay 100mm × 50mm (4in × 2in) timber joists spiked into the plate. If you use 100mm × 50mm joists then the sleeper or dwarf walls should have been built at 1.35m centres.

The flooring grade chipboard is laid directly on to the joists or, having gone this far, you may use tongued and grooved timber boards.

**Doors**
From the floor we pass logically to the internal doors. The overall sizes of the doors will have been decided upon during the design stage but the type of door may be altered as you proceed through the project. Assuming you choose a plywood flush door or a similar sapele veneered article with or without half-hour fire resistance, Figure 46 shows the lipped edge and the central wide mid-rail or lock block. The door needs to be hung on a pair of steel butt hinges; alternatively you can use nylon hinges, and rising butts which lift the door clear of the carpet as it swings open. The door is held in the shut position by a mortice latch. If the door needs to be locked it must be provided with a mortice lock, which comprises both latch and lock. The term 'mortice' implies that the ironmongery is buried in the mid-rail, while the handles locate on to a spindle which passes through the centre of the latch.

The procedure for hanging a door is straightforward. First of all lightly nail the doorstop in position centrally on the door lining. The size of the doorstop varies with taste and with fire resistance requirements. Doorstops can be purchased in sets or can be delivered in running lengths.

Offer up the door and mark with a pencil the exact profile of the opening. Plane to fit. Allow a clearance at the bottom, perhaps by perching

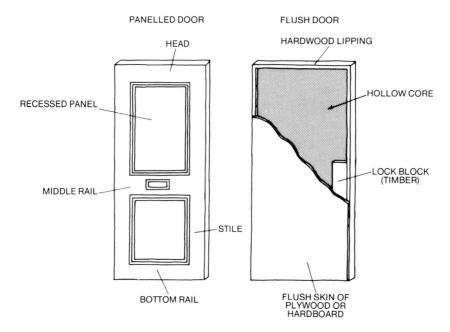

PANELLED DOOR

FLUSH DOOR

HEAD

HARDWOOD LIPPING

RECESSED PANEL

HOLLOW CORE

MIDDLE RAIL

LOCK BLOCK
(TIMBER)

STILE

BOTTOM RAIL

FLUSH SKIN OF
PLYWOOD OR
HARDBOARD

**Fig 46** Diagram of two types of interior door

the door on a batten. Mark the position of the top and bottom hinge 150mm (6in) from the edge, on the door. Sink the hinge into the lip of the door and screw home. Offer up the door plus hinges and carefully mark the screw positions and the shape of the hinges on to the door lining. Chop out the shape of the hinge in the lining. Lift the door into position and screw home the hinges, perhaps with only one of the screws in each hinge. You may have to take the door off again for some final adjustment.

With the door swinging freely, mark the position of the mortice latch in the centre rail. Drill a hole at right angles to the lip of the door, and chisel out a channel to accept the barrel of the latch. Mark the position of the spindle hole, and drill a hole large enough not to foul the free working of the spindle. Assemble the latch plus handles and close the door on to the stop. The last job is to mortice out a slot around which to fix the keep. The door should hold nicely against the stop, which should now be nailed home firmly.

Next is the architrave, which frames the door opening on both sides. This needs to have perfectly mitred corners and must meet the floor exactly. There are many profiles to choose from and the design of the architrave must match that of the skirting board. Each doorway will be the same so by the time you hang the last door it will be perfection. Start upstairs so that the ground floor will reflect your acquired genius.

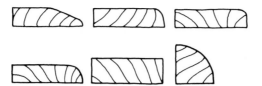

**Fig 47A** Samples of sections of skirtingboard, architrave and quadrant

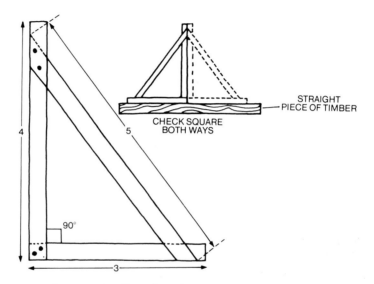

**Fig 47B** Diagram to show construction of a set square

## Skirting Board

The skirting board will be stored in long lengths alongside the architrave and door top. The skirting board completes the joint of floor and wall. The corners must be carefully mitred and care should be exercised at the junction of architrave and skirting. Nail the skirting board to the plastered walls with 100mm (4in) wire cut nails and punch the heads below the surface of the wood. The holes will be filled later. Where two pieces of skirting meet on an internal angle the second piece should be 'scribed' over the first. By this I mean that the exact shape of the one should merge into the other. To make certain that the skirting board sits on the floor precisely, you can press it down using a short plank resting on the top of the skirting and by bearing your full weight on to the plank you will be able to nail it while exerting pressure in a downwards direction.

This covers the fundamental carpentry jobs applicable to most dwellings. There is a whole host of other tasks, such as cupboards, shelves, boxing in of pipework and fitting slatted shelving in the airing cupboard once the hot cylinder has been positioned. All such tasks are so defined by personal taste that I shall leave the self-builder alone to battle over these problems. The urgent matter, after all, is to get the building into a habitable state.

## Sanitary Ware

So we move on into the realms of the plumber. The second fix aspect of the plumber's work can be carried on simultaneously with the carpentry work, should you choose to hire a subcontractor.

The bathroom contains all three widely used sanitary ware fittings. Start by fixing the bath. This will either be made of pressed steel covered with vitreous enamel or cast iron coated with vitreous enamel; there are also plastic and glass fibre baths available. The bath legs must be located on 100mm × 50mm (4in × 2in) bearers, laid flat, and the levelness of the bath may be adjusted by turning the threaded legs. The slope of the bath, to enable it to empty, is incorporated into its shape, but the edge of the bath must be level. We are faced with two copper 'tails' in 22mm (¾in) copper tube to supply the hot and cold taps; tradition has it that the hot stands on the right side of the bath, as viewed by a person sitting in the bath, while the cold tap takes the left side. This rule applies to baths, basins and sinks. The taps should be securely fixed to the horizontal sill at the end of the bath. To the threads protruding beneath the bath we fix a brass bath tap connector, which is a capillary 'Yorkshire' fitting enabling a connection to be made between the tap and the supply pipe. Try to secure the taps before pushing the bath into its final position. Fix the combined overflow and waste (plug) into the holes provided in the bath, bedding each carefully on to a smear of 'plumber's mate'. The outlet trap, which will screw, handtight, on to the protruding waste fitting, must be connected to the soil vent stack by 38mm (1½in) plastic pipe glued at the joints with approved cement (one system is called 'Solvent Weld', which literally fuses the two plastic fittings). The plastic waste pipes are satisfactorily cut with a hacksaw. A gentle 'fall' should be maintained towards the soil vent stack, The latter (100mm) can be cut to the appropriate height and a plastic joiner inserted which possesses two connections for the bath waste and the basin waste. Push the bath into position and make the final connections. The bath is ready to be boxed in with timber framing and plywood or with a manufactured bath panel which comes with the bath.

The wash basin will either be built into a counter top, in which case it is called a vanitory unit, or it will be mounted on a pedestal, or it will be supported on towel rail type brackets. Whichever you have chosen, it will have to be fixed in position, being careful not to overtighten the

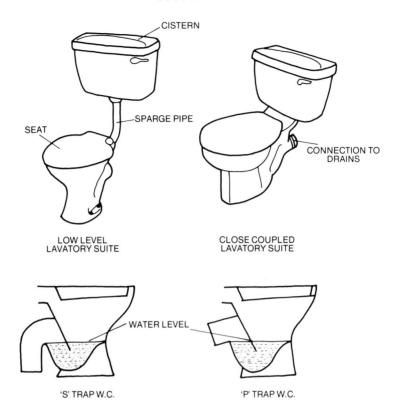

**Fig 48** Sketches of various aspects of washdown water closets

screws in the vitreous enamel fixings points. Bring the 15mm (½in) supply pipes to both hot and cold taps. Assemble the waste and overflow fittings and connect to the spare boss on the soil vent stack.

Last, but by no means least, we must fit the lavatory. There is some confusing terminology surrounding this ugly vitreous china object. The basic pan is described as either an 'S' trap or a 'P' trap, depending on the angle at which the waste comes into the pan. They both rely on a small reservoir of water remaining in the pan to seal off the drain. A 'double syphonic trap' has the advantage of silent operation and there is far less chance of the trap or reservoir of water being emptied by a syphoning action, especially likely in tall buildings. Attached to the pan either directly, in which case it is termed 'close-coupled', or indirectly via a flushing pipe when it is called a 'low-level suite', is the cistern. The close-coupled arrangement is very neat and easy to install. Either way the cistern needs a 15mm (½in) supply pipe attached to it with a cistern connector. This supply can be tee'd off the mains cold supply to the cold side of the bath or basin. Make all the plastic hand-tight joints with some PTFE tape to fill out the threads. Mark the wall behind the cistern in line with the overflow outlet. Drill the cavity and push a 15mm (¾in) plastic overflow pipe through the wall to project 150mm (6in) from the building.

The pan in an upstairs bathroom will need to be a 'P' trap in order to line up with the plastic soil drain. You will have to use a short piece of 100mm (4in) grey plastic pipe to come out of the soil vent stack, followed by a 90° bend, terminating in a magic 'quick-fit' pan connector, which is literally a push fit. Make the quick-fit connection and screw the pan down to the floor with long roundhead screws through the holes in the vitreous china. Do not overtighten.

If you have a shower to plumb in, make sure that you secure the waste fittings before lowering the extremely heavy shower tray into position. Perhaps even raise the shower tray up on support timbers to enable you to reach the waste pipe, to make the union between 38mm (1½in) waste pipe and plastic 'P' trap. You also might need to work on the 'P' trap at a later date if it ever became blocked. Always remember this when you are merrily boxing everything in behind miles of plywood. If it leaks one day, who will have to mend it?

## Hot Water Cylinder

Now we can move out of the bathroom and move back up the supply line to the hot cylinder. The most common hot cylinders are made of copper with a capacity of 40 gallons and with an 'indirect' method of heating the water. This means that the hot water from the boiler, Parkray or back boiler is contained in coils of pipe and is entirely separate from the hot water for domestic use. Each tank will have an immersion heater run off electricity to act as a summer hot water source. The immersion heater should be screwed into the aperture provided using some boss white to make the joint. Tighten carefully with giant steelsons borrowed from the local garage. The electrical connection can be dealt with later. Place the cylinder on 75mm × 50mm (3in × 2in) softwood beams and connect a 22mm (¾in) copper pipe to the compression fitting on top of the cylinder. This pipe will lead up into the roof space and will curve over the top of the cold tank to act as a safety discharge pipe should the water in the cylinder reach boiling point. At a convenient place above the cylinder the 22mm hot supply pipe should be tee'd off the expansion (safety) pipe and thence by a circuitous route to the bath, basin and shower, and downstairs to the sink. The cold supply to the hot cylinder is attached to the bottom compression fitting and this must be 22mm copper pipe. You can only draw off hot water as fast as the cold can run into the bottom of the tank. The cold level rises all the time you draw hot water from the top of the tank, the cold water from the roof space storage tank pushing the hot water out of the top of the cylinder. It is useful to build in a gate valve on both cold and hot water pipes, plus a drain valve at the lowest point, so that you can easily isolate and remove the cylinder should any repairs be necessary; in some cases this is required under waterboard byelaws and this should be checked.

**Radiators**
These come next. If you have already decided on the colour schemes you could give the walls behind the radiators a couple of coats of emulsion before fixing, or you may leave it and use a radiator brush during the decorating phase. Radiators should be positioned at the same height from floor level where possible and should be sited as unobtrusively as the rooms will allow. Radiators are positioned under windows not to heat the garden but to provide the maximum movement of warm air across the room and to be clear of furniture. Most radiators are hung on metal hooks which are plugged and screwed to the plasterwork. The incoming and outgoing radiator valves are then secured with compression fittings which hold the radiator in position.

Mark the centre of the radiator position with a vertical pencil line. Use a spirit level to plumb up the line. Draw a line to correspond with the top of the radiator, again using a spirit level. Measure the bracket positions on the back of the radiator and transfer that information to the wall. Hold the brackets against the wall and mark the screw holes. Drill the wall with a masonry drill bit and insert a plastic wallplug. Fix the brackets firmly and offer up the radiator. Check that it is level, then screw on the bracket using zinc-coated screws.

At the first fix stage we left traps in the first floor floorboards over each branch of the central heating circuit that was destined to link up with a radiator. As soon as all the radiators are in position we can open up the traps and bend the 15mm (½in) pipework, adding a 90° elbow to bring the tail exactly in line with each radiator valve. All tails must go into the valves precisely vertically. Cut and bend the pipes with a small portable pipe bender on hire from the tool hire company. The radiator valves are purchased separately from the radiators. Each radiator needs a 'wheel-head valve' to turn it on and off and a 'lockshield valve' which accepts the return flow pipe to the system. All valves are compression fittings and usually have a chromium finish. Once the compression fittings have been tightened on to the 15mm tube, the radiator will be firmly fixed. Each end of the radiator must be connected to the opposite circulation pipe of the flow and return system. It does not actually matter which way round the radiator is connected; try not to have a brain storm over which pipe is the 'flow' and which the 'return'. As long as each end of the radiator is attached to different pipes you can rest easy.

On the ground floor we have left traps in the timber floor – if it is a timber floor – but if it is a concrete floor covered only by a screed then all carcassing must be left until the moment before the plasterer wishes to lay the screed. If it is you who are attempting both tasks, as I feel it ought to be, then the management is simple. You should have left ducts in the oversite to accommodate the major pipe runs, because the screed alone (75mm) will not be adequate cover for a copper pipe. The ducts in the oversite are easily formed by laying 100mm × 50mm (4in × 2in) timber in the concrete and removing them when the concrete is dry. (Check waterboard byelaws before burying pipes under screeds.)

Place your flow and return 15mm pipes in the ducts. Fix the radiators on to the newly plastered walls as before described. Bring your tails from the flow and the return to each radiator and connect to the radiator valves. When all this pipework on the ground floor is complete you can fill the heating system and test for leaks. If all your joints are dry you can fill the ducts with vermiculite (microfill) insulation granules and then cover the pipes with a layer of sand and cement. Cement must not be allowed to touch copper pipes for fear of chemical attack later. Personally, I hate the idea of buried pipes in concrete screeds beneath layers of costly Wilton carpet. If you must bury the pipes, wrap them in insulating sleeve as well as the vermiculite to be doubly sure of limiting heat loss and preventing corrosion.

The flow and return from upstairs and downstairs meet at the boiler position in the form of four 15mm pipes. The average boiler will present you with four 'tappings': two will receive 22mm pipes to satisfy the flow and return of the primary circuit to the hot water cylinder in the airing cupboard; the other two will take 22mm copper pipes which will be reduced down through a series of simple fittings to accept two flows and two returns from upstairs and downstairs circuits. On this side of the boiler you should install your circulation pump, preferably on the 'return' side of the system.

The two methods of fitting plumbing goods together are enormously simple in the modern era – so simple that the self-builder can confidently assemble his own plumbing. The sanitary ware waste fittings are all plastic screw-on or push-fit, or at worst solvent-weld, which means gluing plastic components much like model aeroplanes. Copper pipe is to be recommended for all 'live' pipework. PVC pipes for hot and cold water have been developed and marketed extensively in the United States but in this country they have made little headway; they tend to be ugly and they need a lot of support. Copper has its own integrity and strength and can even be run on the surface and decorated to good effect. The two methods of joining copper are the 'compression' fitting and the 'Yorkshire' fitting. The compression fitting relies on two brass nuts being tightened on to a threaded centre piece while squashing two soft

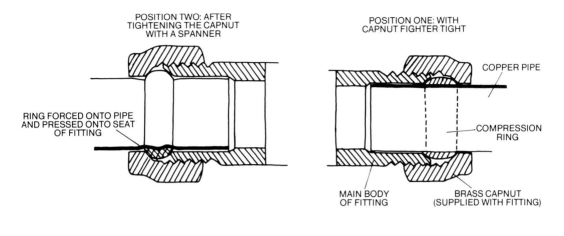

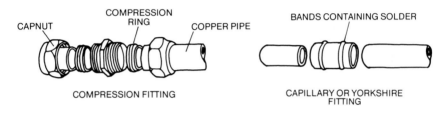

**Fig 49** Diagrams detailing method of joining copper pipe

copper 'olives' on to the pipework, which in turn are drawn by the tightening process into machined brass seats on the centre piece. The Yorkshire fitting or capillary joint is very useful in awkward positions and provides a neat, unobtrusive joint. To use the Yorkshire fittings you need a blowlamp, which in the eighties is a plastic handset connected to a propane gas cylinder weighing about twelve pounds, and a tin of flux (Latin *fluxus* – a flow). Cut the pipe ends neatly and polish with wire wool until they shine. Take the Yorkshire fitting and smear with flux, which serves to protect the solder during the process of heating. Apply flux also to the shiny cut ends of pipe, and push the pipe ends into the fitting. Apply heat evenly from the blowlamp, warming the entire fitting simultaneously. When you see the bright gleam of molten solder appear at the rim of the fitting, the joint is made. Allow to cool and wipe off the surplus flux.

## Kitchen Fittings

The kitchen has been crowned with a high degree of importance in the last twenty years to the extent that the fittings and units and paraphernalia may cost more than a double garage. I shall not enter into the complexities of kitchen design; we are all self-taught kitchen experts and the ergonomics surrounding the work that goes on in a kitchen is much discussed in magazines and specialist books. I think, on the subject of the horrific costs of manufactured kitchens, there are one or two things to add. The brochures and the advertising people teach us to love the laminate finish in all its different shades and colours. However, there are other substances which may show a considerable saving. As I see it you have these alternatives: you can choose a complete kitchen to suit your room, or you purchase standard units and fit them yourself, or you can build the kitchen fittings from scratch.

To follow the latter course of action you need to construct the cupboards in carcass form and then add the cupboard doors and the worktop. This method of in situ construction can apply both to the cupboards beneath the worktop and to the wall units. The accepted standard depth for kitchen fittings is 600mm (2ft) and the height of the worktop from the finished floor level is generally 860mm to 910mm (34in to 36in). Using 40mm × 40mm (1½in × 1½in) prepared timber, set out

**Fig 50** Section through kitchen to show approximate distances between components

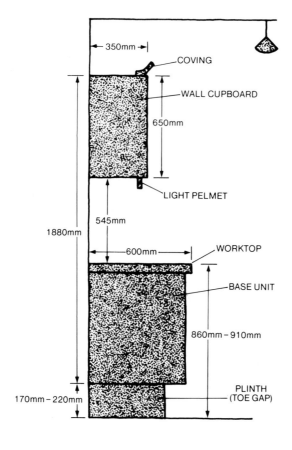

and build a cupboard front to accept either standard doors purchased from a kitchen store or doors made by a friendly joiner to your specification. You might use 19mm (¾in) blockboard with hardwood lipping on all edges. This can be decorated to a high standard and adorned with knobs of your own choice. Perhaps the joiner could make the cupboard front for you. Two horizontal beams should be screwed to the wall. A plinth forms the bottom shelf of the cupboard and must be set back by 100mm (4in) from the finished face of the cupboard to form a toe space. The cupboard front stands off the wall by 600mm and the worktop sits on beams housed over the horizontal member already screwed to the wall. You could mask out the hardwood lipping and spray the doors with cellulose paint before hanging them. The worktop may be slate or marble or could consist of a plywood base with a moulded upstand to receive ceramic tiles. You can hire a carpenter for a week at a cost of perhaps £200 just to ensure that the standard of finish is excellent. My nextdoor neighbour hired an unemployed boat-builder to construct a complete kitchen using mahogany veneered plywood. The quality of her kitchen far surpasses the laminate 'easy-clean' variety, and for half the cost.

The kitchen sink may also be fitted into a carcass of 40mm × 40mm (1½in × 1½in) timber with a cupboard front to match. Wall units may be constructed in exactly the same way. The space between the worktop and the bottom of the wall unit should be about 545mm (21½in) and the wall unit should project about 350mm (14in) from the wall.

How are you going to heat the kitchen? Radiators occupy valuable wall space. Perhaps the room should be designed around a solid fuel appliance to provide a nucleus of heat at all times. Let us suppose you intend to install a solid fuel appliance adjacent to the chimney breast provided in the kitchen. It could be a Parkray or a gravity-fed coal boiler to provide full central heating as well as a warm kitchen, or it could be a pretty little wood-burning stove, to use purely as a room heater and clothes drier. This leads us to the provision of hearths.

## Hearths

These are flat, non-combustible surfaces on which such appliances rest. They must be 125mm (5in) thick and they must fill the area enclosed by the back and jambs of the chimney breast. They must project from the front line of the jambs by not less than 500mm (20in). If your chimney is built on the outside of the building, and you are presented with a flat wall in the room, the hearth must be an area 125mm thick with sides not less than 840mm (33in). The same measurements apply to the hearth in the sitting room or wherever else you have a fire opening.

All the heating appliances come with manufacturers' copious fitting instructions and if you are able to understand this book the instruction leaflets will read like a copy of the Beano. Parkrays and boilers should be connected up to their respective flues and firmly positioned on the hearth and all joints to the flue made good with fire cement, which can be purchased in 1kg or 2kg tubs. It is ready for use. Leave all cladding and side panels to one side until the pipework has been connected between boiler and hot cylinder and between boiler and radiator circuit.

How you finish off an open fireplace largely depends on taste. One very simple way to surround an opening is to build a skin of hand-chosen facing bricks up to mantelpiece height and to find an oak beam from a demolition site to frame the opening. The fixing down of the beam is easily done with two strips of metal strapping similar to the material used as gable restraints in the loft space, perhaps even an off-cut.

## Electrics

As soon as the plaster begins to dry you can fix face-plates to the electrical ring circuit. Clean out the sunken boxes and strip back the outer sheath of the cable. Pare back the red and black wires using a special pair of pliers equipped with gauged teeth which cut the PVC sheath but not the copper wire core. Take the plastic face-plate and loosen the terminal screws. Cover the earth wires in green and yellow hollow sheathing, obtainable in coils. Insert the red (live) wires into the terminal marked 'L', and insert the black (neutral) wires into the terminal marked 'N'. Tighten the screws. Remember you have two reds and two blacks because one cable brings the power into the socket, while the other carries the power on to the next socket in the ring circuit. One pair of red wires shares the same fuseway in the consumer unit, the current feeding both ways into the ring circuit. Next, group the earth wires together and insert into the earth terminal on the face-plate. Also connect a piece of earth wire, suitably sheathed in green and yellow cladding, from the face-plate terminal to the earth screw located in one corner of the knock-out box. This ensures a good earth connection despite the adjustable lugs previously mentioned. Carefully push the face-plate back into the knock-out box and locate the two fixing screws at the side of the socket. Tighten the screws, checking all the time that the socket is level. Repeat this all over the building for all the other socket outlets.

The switch points can be fixed next. Here we have one cable ($1mm^2$) reaching from the switch to the light fitting. That cable contains three wires: one red, one black and one naked earth. For the purpose of switching we are going to use both the red and the black as live wires so we must clearly indicate this by sleeving the black (normally neutral) wire with a red casing. The red wire is connected to one side of the switch, the black is connected to the other side and both are screwed home firmly. The earth wire is treated in the same way throughout the wiring process. If you have a gang of switches operating several lights then apply the same process to each pair of wires.

Complete each room, moving slowly towards the consumer unit position. The unit is mounted on a piece of blockboard which should, eventually, have a cupboard built around it. Make the board large enough to receive additional equipment at a later date. When you remove the cover of the consumer unit containing eight fuseways you will see a large on/off switch, let us assume to the right of the unit. The red and black 16mm² tails will be connected to this and will be left long enough to reach the meter position. There is a plate next to the on/off switch studded with eight screws to which all the black neutral wires are connected. Moving to the left we see the eight parallel fuseways, each with a terminal to receive the red live wires from each of your circuits. At the far left we find another copper plate with eight screws, each awaiting an earth wire from the house circuits. Of the eight fuseways we might have one serving the cooker protected by a 32A fuse, one serving the immersion heater protected by a 16A fuse, one serving each ring circuit protected by a 32A fuse and one serving each lighting circuit protected by a 6A fuse. Thus we have a total of six fuseways used, leaving two spare for future development, which must be covered with a protective shield. Use rubber grommets where the cables pass into the consumer unit and sheath all the earth wires in yellow and green PVC. Make sure that you make the live, neutral and earth connections to the consumer unit in sequence from the on/off switch across the unit.

One last major requirement is to install throughout the building 'earth equipotential bonding', which is designed to protect us further. It means that if a fault occurs and the current is for some reason finding its way to earth via a water pipe or other metal object, the signal will not be felt in the earth leakage protection circuit breaker, or residual current circuit breaker (RCCB), and the current will not be instantly switched off, so that if you were to touch a tap or pipe in this condition, the current would use you as a convenient earthing point. It will always take the easiest path. Equipotential bonding means literally to lift all the metal-work in the building to the 'same potential' for transmitting current back to the consumer unit. To achieve this we must interconnect all pipework: all the sink tops, baths, gas pipes and heating runs must be bonded by attaching earth clips that grasp the pipe, not unlike a sur-clip, and earth wires of not less than 4mm² diameter must be used. The consumer side of the gas meter plus the rising water main must be connected directly to the consumer unit using 10mm² earth wires, and the wire must be continuous. The earth block on the consumer unit will be connected to the electricity company's earth bar inside the meter box. The most common modern form of earthing provided by power companies for their incoming supply is protective multiple earthing (PME), which utilises the neutral wire as the earth facility. This provides a cheaper, more efficient method of earthing the main supply; cheaper because the incoming supply need only consist of two cables, a live and a neutral, and more efficient because it removes the need for each building to have its own earth electrode planted in the ground where it is subject to damage and to corrosion. In a PME system, the incoming neutral and the out-going earth are joined together at the meter position on the earth bar.

With regard to the meter position, it is perhaps worth asking the power company to supply the meter box when they are engaged to provide temporary power for building purposes right at the beginning of the project. You could raise the brickwork where the box is to be sited and build it into the cavity wall there and then. You will have a meter and house fuse connected to a temporary board provided by you, which will have to be housed in a lockable, weatherproof box on the inside wall immediately adjacent to the meter position. Even though the building is nowhere near waterproof, you can easily construct a box to house the electrics safely. On the temporary board you will need to fix an RCCB main control, feeding a fused switch leading to a double socket outlet, complete with an earth stake driven into the ground. You will have to get your application form in to the power company at the planning stage to ensure that electricity is available as soon as you need it.

**Decorating**

A house is not considered to be finished or habitable until it is decorated. The building societies require the decoration to be finished before they will release the final payment.

As soon as the plaster is 'white' dry you may begin painting. Emulsion paint is the best treatment for new plaster as it allows the building to continue to dry out through the surface paint. If you choose to have coving fixed at the junction of ceiling and walls then this should be com-pleted before painting commences. Purchase the lengths of coving in either 100mm (4in) or 127mm (5in) girths. It comes in 3m, 3.6m and 4.2m lengths, and it can be cut easily with a fine-toothed saw. Where coving meets a corner it must be mitred accurately, using a mitre box. Gyproc Cove is made by British Gypsum and comes with a special adhesive in 5kg or 12.5kg bags. You mix the adhesive in a bucket by adding the powder to clean water and stirring it until a smooth paste is formed. Mark a pencil line along the ceiling and wall 67mm from the point where the ceiling meets the wall. These two parallel lines mark the outside edges of the coving. If the girth of the cove is 127mm (5in) then the marks should be 83mm from the intersection of wall and ceiling. Roughen the plaster surface within the guidelines and dampen if the plaster is very dry. Apply the adhesive to the coving. Raise the length of coving and push into position, following the guidelines. Wipe off the surplus adhesive with your finger, at the same time filling the joint, especially where there are mitres. You may need to hold the coving in position with plasterboard nails until the adhesive has set. These may be removed later.

Next attack the woodwork. Dab 'knotting' on to all knots in the wood to stop any resin from exuding after the final coat has been applied. Prime all woodwork that has not already been primed either at the timber yard or on site by you on a rainy afternoon. Next, apply one undercoat. This will have the effect of raising the grain of the wood and highlighting any nail holes or blemishes which need to be filled with Polyfilla or a similar cellulose filler. I am assuming that all nail heads have been punched home. Fill the woodwork using cellulose filler applied with a flat plastic spreader. Allow this to dry and vigorously sand off the surface to a mirror flatness: the standard of paint finish depends upon the early stages of rubbing down and filling. Apply a second undercoat. Rub down with fine sandpaper. Next, move on to the ceiling and walls and apply a 50 : 50 mixture of emulsion paint and water, a 'mist' coat to seal the fresh plaster and to reduce its appetite for paint. Follow this with two coats of neat emulsion. Where there are 'galls' in the plasterwork (areas where the trowel has skipped a patch, creating a moonscape) fill as necessary with cellulose filler and rub down.

When all this is dry you can sweep out the room most carefully and apply a final coat of gloss paint to the woodwork.

The external paintwork may be done as soon as the putty in the windows is hard enough to receive paint. All external woodwork should be protected by two undercoats and one final gloss coat of oil-based paint. If you are using a stain then the joinery must not be primed and manufacturer's instructions must be followed. The fascia-board and soffit may be painted while the scaffolding is still in position.

Paint companies for generations have been striving to market a single-coat paint for exterior use. The acrylic paints are very clever and are designed to allow water to move in and out of the woodwork, giving, as they say, 'life' to the timber. I do not find the argument convincing: in exposed positions and during long grizzly British winters, I think that more rain water would pass into the timber than would pass out. Also, remember when using acrylic paints to use acrylic putty. Oil-based putties will heartily reject an acrylic topcoat.

# 9
# OUTSIDE WORK

With great relief you can turn to the peaceful labour of laying out the garden. The garage may be joined to the house, in which case it would be wiser to build it at the same time as the main house, and it will almost certainly feature strongly in the eyes of the financiers as to whether the building has reached completion. If the garage is separate from the house, it might be wisest to excavate and pour the footings and bring the brickwork out of the ground, and perhaps even go as far as pouring the oversite concrete at the same time as making the concrete subfloor in the main house. This achieved, you could abandon the garage and treat it as a totally separate project, bearing in mind that the planning approval lasts for three years. The cost of a double garage with a pitched, tiled roof will be substantial. Any saving could be used to improve the standard of finish in the house.

I think the garage should be constructed of cavity brickwork. The building may enjoy a change of use at some future date and meanwhile as a garage and storeroom it will be even more dry and sound. There is something decidedly flimsy about a single brick wall. At the present time, the extra costs of cavity walls are negligible. It may be an advantage to construct a loft with steps leading up to a storage space, or it may be possible just to build in the joists and leave the flooring until later.

The driveway will have been punished by heavy lorries during the building work. The edges should be defined with kerbs. If you do not take some trouble over the initial shaping of the drive it will soon lose definition and become untidy. The shape of the drive must be clearly marked with pegs. A shallow foundation trench should be dug with a view to setting concrete kerbs in a concrete foundation, so that the top of the edging kerb finishes just above the final surface of the drive. The concrete is 'haunched' around the kerb, which is put in using a taut building line. The driveway must be filled to within 50mm (2in) of the top of the kerb using 'type two roadfill' (BS1377) from your local gravel pit. Type two roadfill is the name given to material 'as-dug' from the gravel pit, with a stone size of 75mm (3in) down to sand.

If you ask for type two roadfill, the gravel pit will supply their answer to the standard material and it will form a thoroughly suitable base for your drive. I should let this settle for several weeks and then apply a layer of shingle 10mm (⅜in) in diameter and 25mm (1in) thick. This still leaves the kerb projecting 25mm above the finished surface, which will stop the shingle from spreading. Observation during the building project will reveal any drainage problems along the drive. Any low spots can be dealt with using a trapped gulley leading to a small soakaway next to the drive.

Boundary fences fulfil three tasks: they mark the extent of the property, they provide privacy, and they give protection from animals coming in and from children and animals going out. A wire fence is ugly and cheap and provides no privacy. One excellent answer is to erect a wooden board fence mounted on timber rails, which in turn are fixed to concrete fence posts. The concrete posts are 75mm × 75mm (3in × 3in) and stand 1,600mm (5ft 3in) out of the ground. They are buried in concrete at 2m centres and two 100mm × 50mm (4in × 2in) timber rails are then bolted into slots in the side of the post. Feather-edged boards can be nailed to the rails to give a neat, vertically boarded fence against which you can grow shrubs and trees.

Boundary walls need to be 225mm (9in) thick, rising from a foundation constructed in the same way as described for the house. The 225mm thickness allows you to use 'Flemish bond', where a stretcher is followed by a header, or 'English garden wall bond', where one header is laid across the wall and is followed by three stretchers which are laid along the wall, forming an attractive pattern. Instead of 225mm brickwork you could use 450mm × 225mm × 225mm (18in × 9in × 9in) hollow concrete blocks. These blocks have the advantage of providing the 225mm thickness while reducing the mass. They can be rendered on both sides and finished off with an imaginative coping.

All paths and patios must finish 150mm (6in) below the damp-proof course of the house and garage. The main point to concentrate on with any of these surfaces freshly won from the muddy building site is to excavate the area in question thoroughly and remove at least 225mm (9in) of topsoil. Then you must bring in enough type two roadfill or lean-mix concrete (by lean mix, I mean a ratio of ballast to cement of 15 : 1) to firm up the area adequately, and then you can lay the slabs or bricks on spots of mortar, tapping each one level to a building line.

Your topsoil is safely piled on one side of the site. It can now be pulled like a rug over the whole garden, allowing it to lap against the walls and patios and drive edgings. Any surplus can be piled into Himalayan features or used to build a raised bed for vegetable growing.

## 10
# OTHER EXPERIENCES

### Case Histories

Of all the houses built in the private sector of the housing market, one in twelve will be a self-build project. Between ten and twelve thousand houses a year are self-built in Great Britain each year, and the numbers are increasing as the self-build movement gathers momentum.

I give here two examples of successful self-build projects. The first is the experience of a garage owner named Mr Gilby, running a small one-man business in a country workshop. The plot of land next to his workshop became available and he bought it. He gradually worked out a sketch of his requirements and engaged a draughtsman to make a respectable plan with which he could approach the local authority. At the first meeting of the planners the building was passed and the draughtsman then drew the working drawings to satisfy the building control department. Mr Gilby then approached four building societies and the fourth one agreed to finance the project. The building society engaged a surveyor to check the budgets and costings which Mr Gilby had arrived at via a builder's merchant who quoted for all the materials, and various subcontractors who quoted for each stage of the job. A local firm of builders was asked to tender and their figure was £57,500. Mr Gilby decided to proceed along the self-build path using subcontractors for each task and managing the site himself. The building society specified that a surveyor should monitor the progress and authorise payments from them at five stages: (1) oversite completed; (2) completion of first floor joists; (3) roofed in; (4) plastering completed; (5) all works completed. He was able to arrange to finance the first stage up to 'oversite' by obtaining credit from the builder's merchant and by negotiating credit with the groundworkers. Neither were paid until the first instalment was received from the building society.

The self-employed groundworkers recommended a pair of bricklayers who dealt directly with Mr Gilby and who proved to be punctual, careful and cheap. The friendly groundworkers then recommended a carpenter who built a traditional roof with the minimum of help from Mr Gilby. All materials were ordered by Mr Gilby and he was present on site each day to answer queries and to organise the steady flow of materials from the builder's merchant which had originally quoted for the materials side of the contract. Mr Gilby was obviously mining a first-rate seam of local craftsmen. The only building work attempted by Mr Gilby and his wife was the insulating of the roof space and the fixing of the kitchen units. Every other job was carried out by local craftsmen. The building work inclusive of materials, labour and VAT cost £33,000, providing 146m² (1,600sq ft) of habitable space. Mr Gilby will claim back £3,000 from HM Customs and Excise, bringing the cost per square foot down to £18.75. The house was completed in six months, with six further months of planning, making a project time of one year.

Mr Gilby found the day-to-day management of subcontractors tiresome, but he is full of praise for the degree of co-operation between the tradesmen. His house is now valued at £70,000 – a good year's work!

## Self-Build Housing Associations
The second example is an illustration of building your own house by becoming a member of an association. Out of the ten thousand self-build units raised in Great Britain each year, ten per cent will be built within an association. The advantages are considerable. Between ten and twenty people gather together in order to build a house for each person on an estate of houses, using their own labour during their leisure hours. It is a group activity, pooling all the myriad skills and experiences of all the members. The association is registered with the National Federation of Housing Associations, which gives the group legal status. The NFHA produces an excellent publication called the *Self-Build Manual*, which clearly tells you how to set up an association, how to run it and how to obtain finance. Professional advice must be sought to provide accurate costings. This is essential both to satisfy the financiers and to foretell accurately the cost of each unit to the individual within the group, so that he may negotiate a mortgage to buy the unit when completed. This figure per unit is critical because if the costs rise above the budget, the individual may be unable to raise a mortgage due to his earning power or lack of it, and may be forced to sell his unit. The groups usually opt for identical buildings to simplify the whole process of finance, material ordering and daily management. Timber-framed houses are popular owing to the speed at which they can be erected and also because the group may be able to become proficient carpenters, whereas they are unlikely to be skilled enough in the art of bricklaying.

Here is an idea of what is involved using a self-build association near my home as a supreme example of group effort, harmony and success. I am very grateful to the members of the group for the cheerful outpouring of their spirits and for the help they have given me in researching this subject.

The germ of the idea sprang from a parish council meeting where one lively member suggested a self-build project to arrest the flow of young families away from the village. He pinned a notice in the post office and suggested a general meeting of interested parties in the village hall. Twenty people turned up. It was decided to pursue the idea and a committee was formed. The idea had taken root.

The group reduced to fourteen and met each week for a year before a single mark was made in the ground. The first weeks were spent approaching all farmers and landowners to find a site for fourteen dwellings. The local earl offered a field at a market price fixed by the district valuer, and the local authority granted permission to build, in principle. Next the group formed themselves into an association as per the *Self-Build Manual*, produced by the NFHA. They employed the services of a local design consultant who was deemed to possess adequate qualifications to impress the sources of finance. He produced a series of sketch schemes which were laid before the whole group in an extremely professional manner. All fourteen members had to agree to a single design to be used throughout the site. This was, remarkably, achieved at one meeting, and the quest for planning permission was under way. The necessary permissions were granted; access was agreed with highway authority and the landowner; easements for sewage pipes and services were obtained. The design consultant meanwhile prepared comprehensive costings of the timber-framed houses with a brick and tile exterior. The local branch of the Nationwide Building Society was approached and they agreed to finance the project with an option to provide mortgages to the individuals once the project was completed.

The group followed the rules in the *Self-Build Manual* very carefully and a strong sense of discipline was upheld from the beginning. Out of the fourteen men, only three had served apprenticeships in any trades: there were two carpenters and one plumber. All the rest learnt from the three tradesmen so that they were able to divide into teams, each team being led by a craftsman. They dug the foundations by hand because there were at all times fourteen men ready to work. When the oversite slabs were complete the teams were able to raise a timber dwelling and cover the roof with felt within one weekend.

As they settled into the routine of three evenings per week, yielding nine working hours, and every Saturday and Sunday, yielding eleven hours each day (a total of thirty-one hours per week), the unskilled members found their own calling: one carpenter had been appointed site foreman; two men learnt how to do the scaffolding; another man fixed all the vapour barriers and all fourteen men teamed up to do the heavy groundwork. An electrician showed one member how to do the carcass wiring and he was able to wire every house, while the qualified electrician fixed all the face-plates and connected all the circuits to the consumer units. The group hired a gang of bricklayers to build the exterior cladding to each building, this cost being included from the beginning of the project. They drew lots for their houses and were unable to move in until the last house was completed. They kept up the pace of thirty-one hours per week on top of forty hours per week at their jobs, and none missed their quota of hours. A system of penalty fines was arranged, in common with all such schemes, and a schoolmaster was made timekeeper. One man was off sick for three weeks towards the end, but otherwise they all attended the whole time. The building work took fifteen months. The Nationwide Building Society charged half a per cent above the minimum lending rate, as interest, during the building work.

Out of the original fourteen intrepid builders, thirteen still live in their self-built homes. The budget figure for each unit was £14,000 originally and the final cost worked out at £17,000 per unit, inclusive of the land. All VAT was clawed back as the work progressed by virtue of the fact that the association obtained VAT status. Some of the rise in costs were due to the need for deeper foundations on the lower part of the sloping site and extra charges from the bricklayers as the building progressed. This highlights the need for professional help on the estimating stage and for tight management controls while the building is under way.

The members of this association have few regrets. Some wished for a larger plot; some were bruised by the heavy toil on top of their steady jobs. All rejoiced in the comradeship; all agreed that they had achieved far more than they anticipated. Their skills and latent capabilities had been drawn out of them, and they provide a model to association building. They assembled a group of strangers and moulded a team; they followed the management guidelines, sought help in weak areas and housed themselves in properties worth £45,000 by their own initiative.

## Timber-Framed Houses

I feel this is a good moment to bring up the subject of timber framing. It is not new. In the northern states of North America it is unusual to find a brick- or stone-built house. Timber houses achieve high levels of energy conservation. In Britain they are invariably clad with an outer skin of brickwork to fit in with the surroundings. This defeats the object as regards cost and adds very little to the thermal efficiency. The timber-framed house is built in sections at a factory, each section consisting of 100mm × 40mm (4in × 1½in) softwood uprights to suit the room heights, covered with 6mm (¼in) plywood which is in turn covered with a layer of building paper. The sections are specifically designed to the architect's drawings and provide windows and door openings in the relevant panels. The panels are located on the oversite as per manufacturer's diagram and raised into a vertical position, then nailed to the sole-plate (timber) which has been previously bedded on mortar to ensure that it is absolutely level. A Cowley level should be used at this point. Once the ground floor is in place, a layer of 100mm × 50mm timber is fixed to the tops of the panels, spanning all the joins between the panels and ensuring they cannot move laterally. Next, the chamber joists are nailed to the 100mm × 50mm plate and a further sole-plate is fixed on top of the joists. The first floor panels are raised and nailed on top of the sole-plate. Each panel is nailed to its neighbour until the structure becomes strong. At the corners there are stout posts provided to add strength. Next, the wall-plate is nailed to the top of the first floor panels ready to receive the roof trusses.

Vapour barriers of polythene film and fire stops must be built in as recommended all the way through the building. The advantages of timber-framed houses are: speed of erection; the 'dry' method of construction; self-builders are usually more familiar with wood than with bricks and blocks; they are thermally efficient; and the interior does not crack, because it is not plastered but 'dry lined' (plasterboard). The costs of timber versus traditional cavity wall construction are comparable. The disadvantages arise mainly from the way in which the house is erected. The self-builder is going to pay attention to vapour barriers and to correct insulation levels and he is not going to notch the timbers with an axe. The weathering detail where the outer skin of brick meets the window frame may provide a source of trouble: driving rain may penetrate the mastic junction and cause dampness to the window reveals. The windows are normally fixed on brackets to the timber panel and the brickwork is built around the frame later. No one has solved this weakness; the weather seal is dependent upon a mastic joint which may breakdown with age. The NHBC have grappled with this problem and I would refer you to their drawings on page five of the section on timber-framed dwellings in their handbook.

I end by wishing any self-builder bon voyage on his journey through the minefield of bureaucracy into the straight slog of actually building and beyond to the wonderful sense of achievement that accompanies living in your self-built house. I hope the multitude of component parts have been addressed and described so as to make more sense of a jumbled industry. A common fault found in subcontractors in the building world is their reluctance to address a problem in any other way than the method most commonly employed. They are used to working for customers who accept the cheapest path and seldom are they asked to solve a problem in a way that will cost more. Few now serve apprenticeships. To some extent the self-builder can stand against the tide of indifference and take a pride in his shelter.

# FURTHER READING

**Manual to the Building Regulations 1985** (obtainable from HMSO, PC 13A/1, PO Box 276, London SW8 5DT). From the manual you can select approved documents to cover your requirements.

**Registered House-Builder's Handbook,** Part II by the National House-Building Council (obtainable from the National House-Building Council, 58 Portland Place, London W1N 4BU).

**Self-Build Manual,** produced by the National Federation of Housing Associations, 30–32 Southampton Street, London WC2 7AE.

**Building Your Own Home,** by Murray Armor. Especially strong on case histories and self-build associations.

# INDEX

Access, 9, 30, 31, 154
Aggregate, 20–1
Architect, 9–15 *passim*, 17, 20, 36
Architrave, 16, 19, 29, 136–7
Associations, self-build, 9, 17, 153–5; National Federation, 153

Balustrade, 109, 111
Banks, 12–13
Bath, 29, 138
Batten, 90, 115, 129, 130; tile, 19, 26, 94–6, 98, 100, 102
Bead, angle, 116, *116*
Bearing, 24–5, 26, 73, 85
'Bird's mouth', 89, *89*
Blocks, 14, 15, 21–3, 41–2, 62, 72–3, 84, 85, 94, 112, 113
Boiler, 142, 145, 146
Bond, 65, *66*, *80*, 151
Bricks, air, 135; facing, 14, 17, 23, 41–2, 63, 67, 84, 146
Bricklaying, 17, 18, 65, 73, 79–80, 84; cutting, 94
Brickwork, 22, 57, 65–6, 66, 72–3, 79–80, *80*, 94, 150, 155
British Telecom, 54
Building societies, 12, 148, 152, 154

Cables, 19, 27, 54–5, 111, 118–21 *passim*, 146
Carpentry, 19, 106, 107, 134–8
Catnic, 24, *73*, 85, 114
Ceiling, 19, 81, 88–9, 115, 132, 149
Celcon, 23
Cement, 20–1, 129
Cemplas, 42
Cesspool, 48, 51
Chimney, 17, 18, 68–70, 84, 93, *94*, 105, 145; breast, 82, 107, 145
Chipboard, 28, 107, 135
Cistern, lavatory, 139
Clips, 78–9, 104, *104*, 122, 127, 147
Completion of Installation Advice, 118
Concrete, 20–3, 36–40, 58; mix, 39–40, 58, 151; mixer, 40
Connectors, timber, 88
Corners, 65, *71*, 116, 137, 148
Costing, 10–13, 15, 152–4 *passim*
Covenants, restrictive, 8

Coving, 148–9
Cramps, frame, 62, 72, 84
Cupboard, 137, 144–5; airing, 138, 142
Curtain track, 114
Cylinder, hot water, 140–2, 146

Damp-proof course, 15, 18, 22–4 *passim*, 41, *41*, 45, 56, 63, 70, 72, 135, 151
Decorating, 20, 148–9
Design, 14–17
Door, 19, 24–5, 29, 105, 135–6, *136*; frame, 16, 18, 22, 62, 65, *70*, 72; lining, 71, 111–12, 135; lintel, 24; stop, 29, 135
Dorman Long, 24
Drainage, 18, 31, 45–54, *46–50*, *52*, *61*, *62*, *64*, 151; gradient, 46, 48
Drawings, 10–11
Driveway, 30, 31, 150–1

Easements, 8, 154
Eaves, 27, 85, *85*, 96, *96*, 98, 100
Electric work, 19, 27, 106, 107, 117–21, 146–8, 154–5; earthing, 119, 146–8
Environment, Department of, 9
Excavating, 18, 30–1, 35–6, 48, 51, 150–1
Extensions, 14

Fascia board, 26, 88, 96, *96*, 97, 98, 103, 149
Febmix, 42, 130
Fence, 151
'filling', 22, 35, 56, 149
Finance, 10–13, 152–4 *passim*
Fireplace, 68, 68 *see also* Hearth
Fire stops, 156
Flashing, 19, 93–4
Float, plaster, 130
Floor, 15–16, 19–20, 28, 69; solid, 15–16, 58; suspended, 15–16, 22, 58, 60, *60*, 134–5, *134*; boards, 28, 107, 135; first-floor, 25–6, 73, 80–4, 107, 152, 156; sub-, 58, 150
Flue, 146; liners, 23, 69, 70
Footings, 14, 18, 150
Fork-lift, 99–100

Foundations, 18, 20–1, 31, 34–45, *38*, *43*, *45*, 154, 155; depth, 36
Fuses, 118–19

Gable, 14, 17, 18, 84, 92–4, 101, *101*; restraints, 146
Garage, 40–1, 150
Garden, 14, 150–1
Glass, 19, 105
Glazing, double, 7, 16, 105
'Going', 108–10 *passim*
'Green belt', 9
Gutters, 19, 88, 96, 103–5, *104*
Gypsum, 114–15, 130–1; British Gypsum, 114, 148

Hammer, claw, 115; lump, 94
Handrail, 109, 111
Hardcore, 30, 56
'Hawk', 130, 131
Headroom, stair, 109
Hearth, 145–6
Heat loss, 123–6
Heating, 17; central, 17, 19, 27–8, 121, 123–7, *127*
Hepsleeve, 52–3
Hinges, 135–6
'Hockey stick', 118
'Horns', 61–2

Immersion heater, 140
Inspection, 10, 36, 53, 56, 81
Insulation, 7, 15, 17, 28, 142, 153, 156; sound, 44, 112
Insurance, 13, 36

Joinery, 16–17, 20, 60–1, 108–11, 114
Joists, 16, 18, 19, 25–6, 73, 77, 80–4, 82, 83, 107, 120, 121, 135, 152, 156; ceiling, 88–9, 91; hanger, 82, 83; trimming, 82, *82*, 108

Kerbs, driveway, 150–1
Kitchen, 16, 19, 143–5, 153

Land, 7–9 *passim*, 11, 154
Landing, 109–11 *passim*
Latch, mortice, 135, 136
Lavatory, 29, 139–40, *139*

Legal advice, 8, 9
Levelling, 37–9, 156; Cowley, 37, *37*
Lighting, temporary, 106
Linings, 71, 111–12, 116, 135
Lintel, 44, 46, 70, 72–3, 85; box, 73; combined, 73, *73*, 85; door, 24; window, 24–5, 114
Loans, 12–13, 155
Local authority, 7–10 *passim*, 23, 55
Lock, mortice, 135
Loft, 28, 146
Manholes, *47*, 48, *50*, *52*, 53, *61*
Meter, electric, 118, 148
Marley Tile Co, 99
Mortar, 22, 42, 63, 79–80, 84, 102, 128–30; mix, 130; plasticiser, 42, 129
Mortgage, 9, 11, 12, 153
Mouldings, 16
Movement, 15, 51, 84

Nails, lost-head, 107; plaster-board, 115, 116, 120, 149; 'skew', 88; wire cut, 112–14 *passim*, 137
National House-Building Council, 10, 156
Newel post, 109, 111
Noggins, 107
North America, 15, 155
Nosing, 109

'Oversite', 16, 19, 22, 23, *57*, 58, 60, 67, 134–5, 142, 150, 152, 154

Painting, 148–9
Parana pine, 113
Partition, stud, 17, 112, *113*, 115
Paths, 151
Patios, 151
Pea gravel, 51, 53
Pegs, 30, 32–5, 37–9, 150
Pipes, benders, 127, 141; down, 19, 103, 104, *104*; joining, 142–3, *143*
Pipework, 16, 17, 19, 28, 46–54, 103, 107, 121–7, 141–2, 147
Planning, Acts, 7; applications, 9; permission, 8–11, 150, 154; requirements, 7–9 *passim*
Plaster, 120, 128–33; Sirapite, 130–1, 133; Thistle Board Finish, 131–3 *passim*
Plasterboard, 81, 88, 114–16, 131
Plastering, 19, 111, 128–33, 152
Plumbing, 19, 27–8, 106, 107, 121–7, 138–45
Pointing, 80, 102, 103
Preservative, wood, 26, 62, 90, 95, 112
Profile boards, 33–6, *35*, *36*, 42, 43, 45
Protim, 26, 81
Pump, circulation, 28, 142
Purlin, 26, 91
Putty, 19, 149

PVC sheeting, 23, 56, 58

Quantities, 11, 13, 20–7, 37, 56, 100

Radiators, 123, 124, 126, 141–3
Raft, concrete, 36
Rafters, 16–17, 26–7, 84, 89–92, *89*, *91*, *93*, 96, 98; truss, 16–17, 89, 91–2, *92*, *93*, 115, 156
Rainwater goods, 28, 103–4, *104*
'Rawlbolts', 111
Rebates, 16, 70, 113
Redland Tile Co, 99
Regulations, Building, 10, 15, 25–6, 31, 41, 56, 68, 81, 82, 108–10, 123; Electric Supply, 117–18; water authority, 16, 54, 121, 141, 142
Rendering, 19, 129–30
Reveals, 72, *74*, 79, 114, 116, 156
Ridge-boards, 26, 89, 90, 91, *91*
Rights of way, 9
'Rise', 108, 109
'Riser', 108–10 *passim*
Roadfill, type two, 150–1
Roof, 14, 16–17, 19, 84, 85, 87–105, *87*, 152; pitch, 87–8; space, 7, 17, 88, 91, 153
Rusting, 15

Sand, 22, 35, 56, 128–9
Sarking/underfelt, 98
Scaffolding, 18, 24, 73–9, *75*, *76*, *78*, 83, 87, 90, 100, 105, 149, 154
Scandinavia, 14–15
Screed, 16, 19, 20, 142
Screws, galvanised, 24, 141; wood, 62, 113
Scribing, 137
Scrim, 132
'Searches', 8
Services, 9, 18, 54–5, 154
Setting out, 31–5, *32*, *34*
Sewerage, 55
Shoes, 104
Shower, 140
Sink, kitchen, 121, 145
Site, 7–14, 30–5, *33*, 154
Skirting board, 16, 19, 29, 136–7
Soakaway, 46, 103, 151
Soakers, 93–4
Soffit, 84, 85, *92*, 97, 149
Sole plate, 112, 156
Specifications, 20, 128, 132–3
Spot board, 42, 63
Staining, 149
Stairs, 19, 26, 83, 107–11, *108*, *110*
Storage space, 17
Stoves, 145–6
Straps, iron, 86, 94
Stress grading, 25, 81–2, 112
Strings, 109, 110
Strutting, herringbone, 83–4, *83*, 91, 107
Studwork, 111, 112

Sub-contracting, 10, 12, 13, 15, 17–20, 30–1, 74, 105, 106, 117, 118, 128, 132–3, 152–3, 156
Subsoil, 14, 35
Supervision, 10, 12

Tanks, header, 126–7; roof, 28, 89, 140; septic, *46*, 54
Taps, 138
Tendering, 20
Tenons, tusk, 82
Thermal efficiency, 15, 16, 123, 155, 156
Thermalite, 23
Ties, frame, 24; wall, 15, 22, 43–5, *44*, 62, 72, 94; butterfly, 22, 43–5
Tiles, floor, 19, 26–7, 94–103, *95*, *101*; ridge, 27, 100, 102, 103; under-eave, 98, 100; cutting, 103
Tiling, 19, 94–103
Timber, 25–6, 81, 89–92, 111, 112; plate, 85
Timber frame, 14–15, 153, 155–6
Topsoil, 30–1, 151
'Traps', 107, 116, 138–41 *passim*
Tray, cavity, 24, 73; shower, 140
Tread, stair, 109
Trenches, 18, 20–1, 31, 35–45, 150

U-values, 15, 123–5 *passim*
'Undercloak', 102
Unloading, 99–100

Valve, gate, 141; radiator, 141
Vent, soil, 28, 103, 123, 138–40
Ventilation, 17, 28, 103, 123, 124, 134, 135

Wall-plate, 26, 84–6, 88–92, 97, 135, 156
Wallplugs, 111, 113
Walls, 14–15, 40–4 *passim*, *49*, 56–86, *57*, 94; cavity, 14–15, 18, 21–2, 123, 150; garden, 151; internal, 70–4, 84
Wash basin, 138–9
Waterbar, 22
Weather seal, 156; slate, 103
Weep holes, 24, 73
Whitfield, J. F., 118
Winder, 111
Window, 7, 16, 18, 23–5, 60–2, *63*, 65, 72, 84, 105, 107, 112–14, 123, 156; board, 16, 19, 28, 112–14; frame, 60, 156; head, 16, 61, 72, 84; lintel, 24–5, 114; sill, 16, 22, 61, 72
Wiring, 112, 115, 117–21, 146–8, 154
Worktop, 145

'Yorkshire' pipe fitting, 138, 142–3, *143*